Foreword

The psychiatric service in Ireland, as in other Western countries, is based largely on the psychiatric hospitals. These hospitals have for many years provided treatment and care for many thousands of persons with mental problems. Modern treatment methods now make it possible to treat most cases of mental illness in their normal home environment.

This Report, prepared by a specially appointed study group, contains a detailed analysis of our psychiatric service and provides guidelines for its future development as a community-based service meeting, in the most effective way, the psychiatric needs of the population. It is in accordance with a major objective of health policy which has been identified in the Government's National Plan "Building on Reality" which is the shifting of resources from institutional services to community services.

I am pleased to introduce the Report and to invite comments on its contents. Subject to any changes arising from these comments and from subsequent consultations, it is the Government's intention to implement the recommendations contained in the Report. While this must take place within the framework of the allocations for health services which are contained in the National Plan, I am confident that considerable progress can be made towards a realisation of the service described in the Report in the years immediately ahead.

Barry Desmond T.D.
Minister for Health

Contents

Introduction

1. We were appointed as a Study Group by the Minister for Health, Mrs. Eileen Desmond T.D. in October, 1981 with the following terms of reference:

"To examine the main components, both institutional and community, of the psychiatric services; to assess the existing services, to clarify their objectives and to draw up planning guidelines for future development of the service with due regard to cost implications; to carry out such studies and to take part in such consultations as are necessary to assist this examination".

2. The members of the Study Group were:

Mr. Shaun Trant,
Principal Officer, Department of Health (Chairman).

Dr. Fergus Campbell,
Inspector of Mental Hospitals, Department of Health.

Dr. Anthony G. Carroll,
Clinical Director in Child Psychiatry, Western Health Board.

Professor Bob Daly,
Professor of Psychiatry, University College Cork, Clinical Director, Southern Health Board.

Mr. Donal Devitt,
Principal Officer, Department of Health.

Mr. Martin Hynes,
Chief Nursing Officer, St. Mary's Hospital, Castlebar.

Mr. Peter McQuillan,
Chief Executive Officer, South Eastern Health Board.

Dr. Jim O'Boyle,
Consultant Psychiatrist, Eastern Health Board.

Mr. Ronnie O'Sullivan,
Assistant Principal Officer, Department of Health.

Dr. John Owens,
Chief Psychiatrist, St. Davnet's Hospital, Monaghan.

Dr. Dermot Walsh,
Consultant Psychiatrist, Medico-Social Research Board.

Ms. Frances Spillane,
Administrative Officer, Department of Health (Secretary).

3. The Study Group met on 27 occasions, including one two-day meeting. Mr. Patrick O'Sullivan was a member of the Study Group up to December, 1982 when he resigned from his post as Psychiatric Nursing Adviser in the Department of Health.

4. Based on our terms of reference, our objective was to draw up a planning framework for the psychiatric service, to guide future planning and development. To undertake this task we needed to understand the psychiatric service as it now stands, its evolution in recent years and how it is likely to be affected by future events. This was made possible by the first-hand knowledge and experience of members of the Study Group and from discussions with other workers in the service. We also studied a wide range of current literature and the statistical data and reports produced by the Medico-Social Research Board. We referred to the 1966 Report of the Commission of Inquiry on Mental Illness which provided a comprehensive review of the psychiatric services in this country. Indeed our own conclusions are very much in the same spirit as the recommendations of the Commission. We also studied, from the copious literature which has been produced by health and research agencies in many countries and by the World Health Organisation, the latest international trends and developments in psychiatric services.

5. As part of our work, we arranged a series of meetings with the people who provide the psychiatric service throughout the country. We had one such meeting in each of the eight health board areas involving senior professional people of various disciplines. These meetings helped to familiarise the Study Group with the services provided in each area and enabled health board personnel to put forward their views about the changes required. We found these discussions helpful in drawing up recommendations on the future of the service.

6. The main thrust of our conclusions is that the psychiatric needs of the community should be met by a comprehensive and integrated service made up of a number of treatment components and largely located in the community. A number of changes are necessary if this objective is to be achieved. In particular, there must be a decided shift in the pattern of care from an institutional to a community setting with close links between psychiatry and other community services.

7.   We appreciate that our recommendations require some financial investment. We are also acutely aware of the financial difficulties arising from the
current recession and the danger that this will discourage or prevent any
development in the immediate future. We would point out, however, that the
main financial consequence of our recommendations will be a diversion of
current expenditure from institutional to community services rather than an
increase in total expenditure. We would also point out that if our recommendations are not implemented, the capital requirement, in order to maintain the
existing structure, will be much greater.

8.   We have addressed ourselves to the main components of the psychiatric
service, including services for the elderly and for children and services for
alcohol and drug-related problems. There are other specialised areas, such as
forensic psychiatry, and persons with special needs, which we have not dealt
with specifically. A paper on the psychiatric needs of the adult deaf has been
prepared by Dr. Jim O'Boyle who has a special interest in this area and this
paper is included as Appendix 2.

9.   We are satisfied that, although there may be contrary views on some of
the detailed recommendations in our report, there can be little argument
about the general tenor of our findings. What is required now is a programme to
implement these recommendations in all parts of the country. This programme
should be initiated without delay so that mentally ill persons can benefit from
an effective and progressive service.

Acknowledgements
10.   We would like to thank all the people who helped us with various aspects
of this report. We would like to express our particular appreciation of the co-
operation and hospitality we received from the health boards on our visits
around the country in 1983. We are deeply indebted to our Secretary, Frances
Spillane, for all she contributed to the preparation of this report. Her efficiency
and courtesy at all times deserve the highest commendation.

Summary of Main Findings

1. Our aim in this report was to draw up an outline plan of the best service for people in need of psychiatric help. In doing this we had to take account of a number of factors: the successes and the failures in the service provided in past years; the views and experience of those who now provide the service; the existing framework of services; advances which have taken place in our knowledge and understanding of mental illness; the availability of resources having regard to the competing demands of other public services.

2. At present, the psychiatric hospital is the focal point of the psychiatric service in most parts of the country. Large numbers of patients reside permanently in these hospitals. Many of them have lived there for years in conditions which in many cases are less than adequate because of overcrowding and capital underfunding. In addition, staff and public attitudes have tended to concentrate effort on hospital care as a result of which community facilities are relatively underdeveloped. The hospitals were designed to isolate the mentally ill from society and this isolation still persists. The realisation of the psychiatric service which we favour will require many changes. This report describes the changes required and how they can be achieved. The rest of this chapter contains a summary of our main conclusions. In subsequent chapters we discuss each of the major developments in turn.

A Comprehensive Service

3. Every person who needs it should have access to a comprehensive psychiatric service. A comprehensive service is one which caters for the varying needs of people with psychiatric illness. The components of such a service include:

>   prevention and early identification
>
>   assessment, diagnostic and treatment services
>
>   in-patient care
>
>   day care
>
>   out-patient care
>
>   community-based residences

rehabilitation and training

This range of services should be available locally. The different services should be co-ordinated so that a patient can transfer easily from one to another. The psychiatric team should be responsible for ensuring that the services provided by them are integrated with general practitioner, community care and voluntary services. The contribution of general practitioners and other professionals to the primary care of the mentally ill should be supported by the psychiatric teams through the formation of effective working links with them. As far as possible, there should be continuity of professional responsibility between the various services provided by the psychiatric team. The principle of a comprehensive psychiatric service is described in detail in Chapter 2 and the primary care of psychiatric illness is described in Chapter 5.

A Community-Oriented Service

4.   The range of facilities in a comprehensive psychiatric service should be developed to serve the needs of a particular community. The services should be located in the community so that they are close to where people live and work. This kind of service will require some new facilities. These will provide an alternative to the centralised and largely institutional services now in existence which were planned at a time when more modern treatment methods were not available. A community-oriented service emphasises out-patient treatment and day care so that patients can continue to live in their own homes. The need for professional services to provide support for the families of patients living at home is also recognised. The principle of a community-oriented service is described in Chapter 3. The organisation of day care services is described in Chapter 6 and the organisation of out-patient clinics in Chapter 8.

A Sectorised Service

5.   The provision of a comprehensive psychiatric service to a population of a known size within geographical boundaries is an important step in developing locally based psychiatric services. A service organised in this way is described in this report as a sectorised service. A multidisciplinary psychiatric team should be based in each sector with responsibility for providing the required services. The precise size of the sector will depend on local circumstances and on factors such as the centres of population in a particular area and existing administrative boundaries. Subject to the consideration set out in paragraph 4.6, we recommend a population size of 25,000 — 30,000 in each sector. Some services will need to be developed for more than one sector. Such centralised services might include, for example, in-patient services and services for elderly mentally infirm persons. The principle of a sectorised service is described in Chapter 4.

In-Patient Service

6. In-patient treatment for all admissions should ideally be provided in psychiatric units in general hospitals. This is a long-term goal and in the meantime the psychiatric hospitals will continue to provide much of the in-patient service for mentally ill persons. More treatment facilities for mental illness in the community should reduce hospital admissions and in time psychiatric hospitals will play a less dominant role. Comprehensive rehabilitation programmes in the hospitals will result in the transfer of some patients to live in the community and will also reduce in-patient numbers. The decline in importance of the psychiatric hospital will take place gradually and as part of a planned progression to a community-oriented service, in which the in-patient facilities will be small and will function as one element in a network of co-ordinated services.

7. In the immediate future in-patient facilities, whether located in a psychiatric hospital or in a general hospital, will cater for a designated catchment area consisting of a number of sectors. With the increasing availability of a wide range of community services, the majority of patients requiring in-patient admission will be discharged in a reasonably short space of time. However, even with the expansion of community facilities, there will still be a small group, usually described as "new long-stay patients" who, despite active treatment and rehabilitation, will need long-term in-patient care. To ensure that a time will come when the psychiatric hospitals are no longer needed, the psychiatric services in each health board area should begin to provide long-stay care in a more appropriate setting. This means that new facilities for new long-stay patients will have to be established as a matter of priority. The number of places required will be small and we recommend the development of high support hostels for these patients. The future provision of in-patient services for the mentally ill is described in Chapter 7.

Admission Policies

8. In a comprehensive psychiatric service, admission of patients to hospital should take place only after the psychiatric team is satisfied that treatment on an out-patient or day basis is not possible. Psychiatric hospitals and psychiatric units in general hospitals should have screening procedures to prevent inappropriate admissions.

Housing Programme

9. As many as possible of patients who now live in psychiatric hospitals should be provided with housing in the community. This will involve:

—a detailed assessment of patients to establish their level of handicap and their potential for rehabilitation;

—a training programme for patients with special emphasis on social skills training to enable them to cope with the demands of everyday living;

—the acquisition of various types of accommodation for patients who, following rehabilitation, are considered capable of living in the community.

The organisation of a housing programme and various types of community residences are described in Chapter 9.

Improving the Quality of Life for Patients in Psychiatric Hospitals

10.   The psychiatric hospitals must not become forgotten places. Despite declining numbers, they will still be needed for some years and they must therefore be adequately maintained. The physical conditions in the hospitals have been gradually improved as a result of the special minor capital allocations of the past three years. This special funding will continue up to 1987. By then, standards in most hospitals should have reached an acceptable level while the problems stemming from overcrowding will be alleviated as in-patient numbers decline. In the immediate future, the assessment of all patients and the introduction of comprehensive rehabilitation programmes will mean that psychiatric hospitals will be more active than in the past. Patients who are not suitable for discharge to community accommodation need rehabilitation programmes within the hospital. In this way any potential for improvement will be realised and the provision of active therapy will enhance the quality of their lives. Rehabilitation services both in the hospital and in the community are described in Chapter 10.

Needs of Special Groups

11.   We examined separately the needs of a number of special groups. The future provision of services for the elderly, for children and adolescents and for persons with alcohol or drug-related problems is described in Chapters 11, 12 and 13 respectively.

Staff Motivation

12.   The support and commitment of the staff are essential if the comprehensive, community-oriented psychiatric service described in this report is to be achieved. The introduction of comprehensive rehabilitation programmes for all hospital patients will be one of the main areas of activity for many psychiatric nurses in future years. As services become more community-

oriented, so too will the medical and nursing staff currently employed in the service. At all stages in the transition to the new pattern of service, staff should be consulted at every level. They should be involved in the planning process and they should feel confident about their role in the new services. Leadership of a high quality at senior medical, nursing and administrative levels will be necessary to motivate staff to bring about the necessary changes. Staffing questions are discussed in more detail in Chapter 14.

Cost Implications

13.   In accordance with our terms of reference, the cost implications of our recommendations are discussed in Chapter 15.

Planning the Services

14.   Each health board should draw up an outline plan for the psychiatric service. This should include targets and objectives to be reached in 10 to 15 years time, perhaps in five year phases. Priorities for the future development of the service should be clearly identified and energies directed to achieving these priority measures as quickly as possible. Information on therapeutic advances or on changes in the community being served should be regularly appraised and evaluated. The plan must be flexible and should be broad enough to allow for modification as circumstances or attitudes change. The process of planning and evaluation is described in Chapter 16.

Chapter 1

Recent Developments in the Delivery of Health Care for Mentally Ill Persons

1.1   During this century important changes have taken place in the organisation and delivery of services for the mentally ill, changes which are worldwide and which are not yet completed. Among these changes are:

1. a broadening in the scope of psychiatry to encompass a much wider spectrum of mental illness such as neurotic and psychosomatic disorders;

2. a realisation that custodial care of patients in a psychiatric hospital is not the only way, and probably not the best way, of treating mental illness;

3. the development of a variety of alternative community-based facilities to enable mentally ill persons to be cared for at home;

4. a change from passive, custodial care of the mentally ill to active treatment of their illnesses and to the development of treatment and rehabilitation programmes.

Patients in Psychiatric Hospitals

1.2   In 1896 there were 11,000 patients, including mentally handicapped and geriatric patients, in Irish psychiatric hospitals. By 1945, the year the present Mental Treatment Act became law, the number had risen to 19,500. Numbers continued to increase slowly until they peaked at more than 21,000 in 1958. Since then, there has been a steady decline and on 31st December 1983 there were 11,906 patients in health board psychiatric hospitals and units.[1]

1.3   This pattern of expansion and contraction of hospital numbers is common to most European countries. Throughout the nineteenth and early twentieth centuries there was a growth in the numbers of mentally ill in hospital throughout Europe. Numbers in hospital in England and Wales, for example, peaked in 1955. This growth was followed by a fall, giving rise to a celebrated projection by Tooth and Brooke that if the decline continued at the rate shown in the years immediately following 1956, bed rates in England and Wales would be halved in 15 years.[2] This forecast was subsequently proved correct. It must be noted, however, that despite an initial ratio of beds to population which was twice that of England and Wales, the rate of decline in Ireland from 1961 to 1983 has not been significantly greater than in England and Wales.

1.4   The international bed to population ratios varied greatly. Ireland was distinguished by its high ratio. The Report of the Commission of Inquiry on Mental Illness of 1966 pointed out that "In Ireland approximately 7.3 psychiatric beds were provided in 1961 per 1,000 of the population; this rate appears to be the highest in the world and compared with 4.5 in Northern Ireland, 4.6 in England and Wales, 4.3 in Scotland, 2.1 in France and 4.3 in U.S.A. At any given time, about one in every 70 of our people above the age of 24 years is in a mental hospital".[3] It might have added that in some parts of the country the bed to population ratio was considerably higher than the national figure.

Development of Community Facilities

1.5   The main concern of 19th century providers of care for the mentally ill was to ensure that every mentally ill person, and certainly all those who might be thought to be "dangerous lunatics", should be behind walls. The aim was to protect both the patient and society. There was little concern for, or even awareness of, the need to provide care for the mentally ill outside of hospital. However, around the turn of the century there were some stirrings in this direction and one distinguished superintendent, Dr. Connolly Norman of the Richmond District Lunatic Asylum, was moved to say "In the huge asylums which have sprung up or are now springing up everywhere, individual treatment — the one thing likely to benefit our patients — becomes almost impossible".[4]

1.6   The 1945 Mental Treatment Act made the first gesture towards an alternative to in-patient care in this country. It introduced the concept of "parole" or permitted absence for detained patients and provided for "boarding out" of mentally ill patients. Section 24 of this Act allowed for the provision and maintenance in the district mental hospital or elsewhere of consulting rooms or out-patient clinics. The first reference to the establishment of such clinics is in the Report of the Inspector of Mental Hospitals 1949. By 1950, 60 such clinics had been approved by the Minister for Health. Most of the clinics had been established at general hospitals or dispensaries and it was felt that "In such cases the fact that the premises in which the clinics are held are not identified solely with the treatment of mental disorders is undoubtedly great encouragement to persons to attend who might otherwise fail to seek treatment if it were necessary in the first instance to go to a mental hospital".[5]

2

The Commission of Inquiry on Mental Illness was able to report that psychiatric out-patient clinics were being held at 142 locations in 1965 with 25,395 patients making 83,719 attendances.

1.7 From the 1960's onwards, hostels, group homes, day hospitals, day centres, sheltered workshops, rehabilitation and retraining centres were all developed. These were further evidence of the move from the hospitals to the community which has been the trend in psychiatric care since 1945. The extent to which these developments took place varied greatly from area to area throughout the country.

Legislation and Reports

1.8 The Mental Treatment Act, 1945 marked an important legislative advance. In addition to allowing for the treatment of mentally ill persons outside hospital, it also introduced voluntary admission to a psychiatric hospital. This was an important step in removing the barrier between the community and the hospital which had existed up to then. More recently, the Health (Mental Services) Act 1981 was passed by the Oireachtas but it has not been brought into force and it is being reviewed at present.

1.9 The Report of the Commission of Inquiry on Mental Illness in 1966[3] was a major step forward in planning services. The Commission, in proposing to change the image of psychiatric hospitals as the sole centres of care said:

> "the improvement of services and their extension into the community should make the greatest impact. Community care is undoubtedly desirable but its success depends upon the development of a number of specialist facilities within the community".

The Commission then listed the elements which constituted community care and recommended their provision. It noted that one day hospital had already been established in Dundalk and it recommended that the number of day hospitals should be increased. It is worth remarking that the Commission envisaged a substantial role for the primary health care services in the treatment of mental illness and commented "if community care of the mentally ill is to be effective the general practitioner has a vital part to play".

1.10 Other reports dealing with the needs of persons likely to find their way into psychiatric care appeared in the 1960's and 1970's. Foremost among these were the Report of the Commission of Enquiry on Mental Handicap (1965),[6] the Report of an Interdepartmental Committee on the Care of the Aged (1968)[7] and the Third Interim Report of the Interdepartmental Committee on Mentally Ill and Maladjusted Persons (1978)[8] which dealt with the treatment and care of persons suffering from a mental disorder who appear

3

before the courts on criminal charges. In 1980 the report "Services for the Mentally Handicapped"[9] was published. This set out a planning framework for services for the mentally handicapped and argued against retaining these patients in psychiatric hospitals.

1.11   Similar reports, recommendations and policies appeared in other European countries, reflecting the change from custodial to therapeutic and rehabilitative care, based mainly in the community. In England and Wales legislation on mental illness in 1959 was followed by a hospital plan in 1962[10] which stressed the importance of community care. In 1974 the Department of Health and Social Security (D.H.S.S.) published the proceedings of a conference entitled "Providing a Comprehensive Psychiatric Service for the Adult Mentally Ill"[11] and in 1975 published a comprehensive planning document.[12] This report "Better Services for the Mentally Ill" laid down in more detail than previously the requirements of the mentally ill for in-patient and community care.

1.12   In May 1978 the Italian Parliament passed a radical new law. This provided for comprehensive community-oriented mental health services and included directives for the eventual closing down of all psychiatric hospitals. "Alternative Structures" in the community were to replace those provided by the hospitals. Psychiatric wards in general hospitals were allowed; they could have up to fifteen beds per 200,000 population and had to be associated with community mental health centres.[13] The success in implementing the new law has been uneven however and a recent review has suggested that the reforms affect only limited areas of the country. Alternative community services have not been developed by many local health authorities and conditions for patients remaining in the psychiatric hospitals have deteriorated. A new law to replace the law of 1978 is already in draft.[14]

1.13   In short, although doubts were being expressed about the reliance on psychiatric hospitals for the care of the mentally ill at the end of the last century, no alternative was proposed until the 1940's and little provision made before the late 1950's. Where alternatives have been provided they are often unequally distributed and while some areas are well supplied with community facilities, in other areas there are considerable inadequacies.

Treatment of Mental Illness

1.14   Many improvements in the treatment of mental illness were made possible by the advent of drug therapy in the 1950's and early 1960's and the introduction of new psychological and social therapies. Anti-psychotic and anti-depressant drugs reduced the amount of disturbed behaviour among hospital patients and enabled some to be discharged. Those who remained in hospital benefited from less congested living conditions. Large wards, which had previously accommodated all categories of patients without distinction of condition or treatment, were divided into smaller specialised wards.

"Open-door" Policy

1.15   Advances in the treatment of mental illness led to the new community-oriented approach towards the psychiatric service which developed in the 1950's. With the aid of the new drugs, the psychiatric service could treat and cure many forms of mental illness. Staff attitudes changed and the mentally ill were regarded as persons with identifiable medical problems which responded to treatment. As the need to isolate and control mentally ill patients lessened, the psychiatric hospitals began to open their doors and support services in the community for the care and treatment of the mentally ill were developed.

Staffing

1.16   Among the most important changes in the psychiatric service were those relating to the staff providing the service. In general, the staff consisted of psychiatrists and psychiatric nurses working fulltime in the psychiatric hospitals. Their primary role was to segregate patients for their own protection and for the protection of society and to cater for their basic needs. The nature of this work and the authoritarian approach of staff fostered a dependence among patients on psychiatrists and nurses. In recent years, and particularly since the development of new treatment methods, the work of psychiatrists and nurses has become more challenging and positive. The psychiatrist or nurse no longer has a largely custodial role but is concerned with the active treatment of patients using various therapies.

1.17   In addition to changes in the nature of their work, a number of other developments have affected staff in recent years. Firstly, the scope of psychiatry has been seen to include not only the large number of psychotic patients but also the larger number of neurotic and psychosomatic disorders. Secondly, recognition has been given to psychiatry in the academic world and university chairs in psychiatry have been established. Psychiatry has been included as an important component in under-graduate medical training so that all emerging doctors now have some psychiatric training and a better understanding of the needs of persons who are mentally ill. Thirdly, the social, occupational and rehabilitation aspects of mental illness have been identified and it is now accepted that many disciplines are required for comprehensive care and treatment. This has resulted in the development of multidisciplinary teams for the treatment of mental illness. The team comprises psychologists, social workers, occupational therapists and others in addition to psychiatrists and nurses. Fourthly, the role of the psychiatric nurse has expanded to include work in the community. Psychiatric nurses working in the community provide an important link between the specialist psychiatric service and the general community health services.

General Hospital Psychiatric Units

1.18   The provision of acute psychiatric units in general hospitals was another important development in the treatment of mental illness. General hospital units were recommended by the Commission of Inquiry on Mental Illness in 1966 which considered that "the needs of short-term patients can best be met by psychiatric units in, or associated with, general hospitals".[3] The Fitzgerald Report of 1968 on the general hospital system recommended that "a psychiatric service for short-stay patients be provided in every hospital".[15]

1.19   The establishment of psychiatric units at general hospitals has helped to integrate psychiatry with general medicine and also to give recognition to psychiatry as a medical specialty. These units have acquired an acceptability with the public which has never been enjoyed by the psychiatric hospitals. In general, patients are more willing to be admitted to these units than to the psychiatric hospitals. Among psychiatrists and psychiatric nurses the general hospital units tend to have a rather elite status. Some units, unlike the psychiatric hospitals, do not cater for a particular catchment area.

Rehabilitation

1.20   Rehabilitation in psychiatry is concerned with returning skills to a person who has had them impaired by mental illness. The degree to which these skills have been impaired varies from case to case. The capacity to recover, even with the best rehabilitation available, depends mainly on the severity of the illness. While the value of occupation for the mentally ill was recognised as far back as 1810 it was not until the mid 1940's that there was a general revival of occupational measures in the treatment of the mentally ill. At a later stage industrial therapy and retraining were seen as important and industrial therapy units were provided at psychiatric hospitals. Patients were trained to do various types of work in these units and they became familiar with normal work practices. The health boards, together with the Rehabilitation Institute and many other voluntary agencies have been active in providing vocational rehabilitation services for the disabled.

1.21   In recent years, it was recognised that too much emphasis was being placed on vocational training for psychiatric patients rather than work skills forming only one component of a comprehensive rehabilitation programme. The trend towards a community-based psychiatric service highlighted the

6

need for psychiatric patients to acquire social skills so that they could live independently. A report of a Working Party in 1981 on the development of rehabilitation services within the psychiatric service stressed the need to provide comprehensive rehabilitation programmes in every hospital ward.[16]

Extent of Mental Illness in Ireland

1.22   An attempt to measure the extent of mental illness in this country is made in Appendix 1. Hospital data and data from the Three County Case Register operated by the Medico-Social Research Board are analysed. However, both of these sources relate only to cases of psychiatric illness reported to the specialised services and information on the extent of morbidity in the community in general in this country is not available. Estimates from community surveys carried out in other countries suggest that the prevalence of mental illness could be of the order of 10% of the population.

Statistics on Psychiatric Services and Staffing

1.23   In Appendix 3 statistics on the present level of in-patient and community psychiatric services and on staffing in each health board area are presented.

Outstanding Problems

1.24   While the changes which have taken place in the services for mentally ill persons have done much to make these services more relevant to those who need them, the psychiatric service is still below an acceptable standard.

1.25   Despite the decline in numbers, there is still a large resident patient population in the psychiatric hospitals. Many of these people either do not need to be in hospital or, as in the case of mentally handicapped persons, are inappropriately placed in a psychiatric hospital. The policy of moving these patients to accommodation in a community setting should be pursued more forcefully. It is accepted, however, that some of the more seriously handicapped patients who are very dependent on institutional care would not benefit from discharge and their needs will best be met by in-patient treatment.

1.26   For patients who continue to live in the psychiatric hospitals, either temporarily or indefinitely, a wide range of programmes of activation and rehabilitation is needed, whether to prepare them for a more independent life in a community setting or to raise the quality of their lives in hospital. Two categories of patients need special consideration. These are the mentally handicapped, particularly the more seriously handicapped, and elderly persons, many of whom have grown old in the hospital and who may not need active psychiatric treatment.

1.27   Dynamic leadership at senior medical, nursing and administrative level in the psychiatric service is necessary if patients are to move from a hospital to a community setting and if the general level of activity of the remaining patients is to be improved.

1.28   Many of the hospital buildings are old and have poor facilities. Improvements are urgent and necessary in the interests of the patients and staff who live and work in these buildings. The danger is that, as hospitals are improved, admissions of certain categories of patients may increase and the dilemma is how to bring about these improvements without perpetuating the form of care which has become associated with the hospitals.

1.29   The specialised nature of psychiatry tends to make it self-sufficient and to set it apart from other medical specialties. This dichotomy has been aggravated by the isolation of the psychiatric hospitals. Yet, for many reasons, psychiatry needs to be associated with other services, particularly at community level.

1.30   While the principle of building up the community services is now generally accepted, there is a long way to go before these can be regarded as satisfactory. Well developed community services are a prerequisite to achieving a decline in the hospital population.

1.31   If more patients are to transfer from the hospital to the community, psychiatric staff, particularly psychiatrists and nurses, must give an increasing share of their time to services in the community.

1.32   A large number of people with psychiatric problems are being treated by general practitioners. There is a need for better communication and co-operation between the specialised psychiatric service and general practitioners.

1.33   The general public has not yet fully accepted that persons with certain types of mental illness should live among them. The importance of the public's contribution to caring for and rehabilitating such persons is not generally understood. Political and community leaders, supported by professional staff, have a particular responsibility to promote a better awareness and understanding among the general public about people who have been mentally ill.

Chapter 2

Comprehensive Psychiatric Care

2.1 Mental illness encompasses many disorders of varying severity requiring a variety of care and treatment arrangements. To provide comprehensive care, the psychiatric service must foster and support the potential for care and healing within the community. To do this, the service should liaise with, support and help develop the ability of primary health care workers, (particularly general practitioners and community care personnel) to treat people with mental illness. The psychiatric team should build on this infrastructure of care and treatment and provide specialist assessment, treatment, day care, residential, rehabilitation and training services.

Multidisciplinary Approach

2.2 Different approaches to treatment and the participation of people from a number of professional disciplines are required to cater adequately for the needs of the mentally ill. Each psychiatric team should have a consultant psychiatrist as its leader and should include the services of psychiatric nurses and have access to the services of clinical psychologists, social workers, occupational therapists and a health administrator.

Continuity of Care

2.3 There should be, as far as is practicable, continuity of professional responsibility running through the different treatment services provided by the psychiatric team. For example, a patient who is discharged from hospital may need to attend at an out-patient clinic or day facility for some time but he or she should remain under the general care and supervision of the medical and nursing staff who provided treatment in hospital.

Co-ordination of Services

2.4 The components of a comprehensive psychiatric service should be co-ordinated effectively so that the needs of each patient are considered in the context of all available services. Facilities must be organised in a way which encourages patient movement from one component to the other as needs change. There is a need for co-ordination at two levels: firstly, within the psychiatric service and secondly, between the psychiatric service and the general practitioner and community care services. It is important that a patient who is moving from one type of facility to another, for example from a day centre to a workshop, should be able to do so without delay. The responsibility for ensuring a smooth transition by the patient from one facility to another rests with the sector psychiatric team. Liaison with the patient's family and rehabilitation and other agencies is required to achieve proper co-ordination of services.

2.5   In Chapters 5 to 13 we identify the service components of comprehensive psychiatric care and we deal with each part in turn. This approach does not imply that in practice any of these component parts can be considered independently. Comprehensive care as we conceive it, and as it is now evolving, requires the integration of these different services into a coherent whole. In this way the patient can gain optimum benefit from the services available.

2.6   Recommendations

1. **The psychiatric service should be comprehensive so that the needs of all categories of persons with mental illness are catered for (para. 2.1).**

2. **There should be a multidisciplinary approach to the treatment of mental illness (para. 2.2).**

3. **Continuity of care for the patient should be provided as far as is practicable throughout the different services provided by the psychiatric team (para. 2.3).**

4. **The various elements of a comprehensive system of care should be effectively co-ordinated so that patients can be placed easily in the facility most appropriate to their immediate needs (para. 2.4).**

Chapter 3

A Community-Oriented Service

Definition

3.1   By a community-oriented service, we mean a service providing a full range of treatment to persons with psychiatric problems with minimum disruption to their normal way of life. This defintion implies that most patients should not be admitted to hospital, and that treatment services should be delivered to them in their normal social environment.

3.2   The general policy of the development of community care to replace an exclusive programme of hospital care was acknowledged in a World Health Organisation (W.H.O.) report entitled "Changing Patterns of Mental Health Care" [1] where the following recommendation was made:

> "The running down of existing mental hospitals should be phased so as to overlap with the building up of community-based services. In no case should the chronically ill or handicapped person to discharged from hospital until or unless adequate supporting services are provided in the community".

3.3   Research has shown that many patients with chronic psychiatric disability can cope successfully in the community if provided with appropriate support.[2] It has been possible to provide a range of community supports for the chronically disabled, so that it is the exceptional patient who still requires long-stay hospital care.

Advantages of a Community-Oriented Service

3.4   A community-oriented service for the mentally ill has many advantages. Treatment in the community does not result in a break with the patient's family, work and other social commitments. A more realistic assessment of a person's illness can be made. Disturbed behaviour can be much more appropriately assessed in the family setting and with a knowledge of the person's family and socio-economic circumstances. Treatment at home also prevents the growth of dependency in a patient. It enables him to maintain

11

his independence and sense of personal responsibility. Treatment at home mobilises local and family support which are nearly always available, and avoids the "closure" on the part of relatives which can take place if the patient is admitted to hospital.

Mobilising Help in the Community

3.5　It is important to remember that the great majority of mentally ill persons have always been cared for outside of hospital. A large part of this care is provided by persons without professional training in psychiatry. The level of help and understanding shown to the mentally ill by their family, friends and workmates has a great influence on their recovery. One of the tasks which must be undertaken in organising a community-based service is to maximise the help which is available from relatives and friends of the patient and from community workers, voluntary organisations and the public at large. Psychiatric personnel should be active in the local community and should encourage and assist individuals or groups in their efforts to offer support to mentally ill people living among them.

Support for the Families of Mentally Ill Patients

3.6　A survey of long-term users of the community psychiatric services in Camberwell, London investigated the role of relatives in supporting patients and drew up recommendations on the need for extra services where relatives are involved in the care of patients.[3] It was found that the main support given by relatives to patients was firstly, in the area of self-care e.g. washing and dressing, eating, doing housework, managing money, social and leisure activities, taking medication and secondly, in coping with difficult or publicly embarrassing behaviour, attention-seeking, disturbance at night and suicidal attempts, including self-poisoning.

3.7　The main burden of caring for a mentally ill person in the community, particularly a chronic psychotic patient living at home, may fall on the patient's family and the cost to the family, in terms of emotional stress, can be considerable.[4] While home treatment may be best for the patient, this may be disturbing to other family members. The professional service should accept some responsibility for the welfare of the family as well as that of the patient. Family support by psychiatric personnel should include education about the nature of the illness, advice and guidance on the care of the patient and a facility to relieve the family of the care of the patient for designated periods and in times of crisis.

3.8　A study in England[5] has shown that the development of community-based services imposes a considerable burden on the relatives of some patients.

12

It also found that relatives tended not to complain about their problems out of a sense of obligation and due to the low expectation they had of the services available. Relatives often have to cope with problems similar to those of staff in residential and day units. It is important, therefore, that the needs of supportive relatives are considered in planning the service. The families of patients who live at home might be regarded as part of the psychiatric team and the services of the other members of the team should be made available to them.

3.9   In the case of patients with non-psychotic psychiatric problems, the role of the psychiatric team will include assessing the influence of other family members and the home environment on the patient's condition and trying to adjust family attitudes as required.

3.10   We consider that, in planning community-based services, particular attention should be paid to the following points relating to the families of patients living in the community:

1. The psychiatric team must have a commitment to supporting the relatives of patients who live at home. Relatives should be given practical assistance and advice on the problems they encounter such as management of difficult behaviour.

2. The community nurse should provide the link between the family of the patient and the psychiatric service. As well as offering advice and assistance, the nurse or social worker should provide emotional support by developing a continuing relationship with the patient's relatives. Before a patient is discharged from the hospital, the nurse can do valuable groundwork in preparing the family for his or her discharge by, for example, advising on the type of problems which may arise.

3. Day care suited to the needs of the individual should be provided for those patients living at home who would benefit from such care as a valuable support to the family during the daytime.

4. As relatives are centrally involved in caring for the patient, they should be given a role in assessing progress and in planning care. Their knowledge and judgements should be taken into account by the psychiatric team.

5. Arrangements should be made to provide alternative accommodation on a short-term basis for patients so that their relatives can go on holiday or take a weekend break from time to time.

6. Support should be readily available to families in the event of a crisis.

Development of a Community-Oriented Service

3.11   In recommending a community-oriented psychiatric service, we can learn from the mistakes which have been made in other countries where efforts to move chronic hospital patients into the community have been criticised. It has been argued that patients were discharged too soon from the psychiatric hospitals; that they were inadequately prepared for the more independent life they were expected to lead in the community; that adequate support services such as day facilities were not available in the community; that many ex-hospital patients had nothing to do during the day and became inactive and isolated; that there was a lack of co-ordination between the various agencies in the community providing for the needs of former in-patients.

3.12   The policy of caring in the community for persons with varying degrees of mental disability will require the development of a variety of community-based services. This involves:

1. achieving the type of comprehensive integrated psychiatric service outlined in Chapter 2; patients should have access to various treatment services and should be able to move easily from one to another;

2. establishing links between the psychiatric service and the community care service; in particular, it is important that there should be full and effective collaboration with public health nurses and general practitioners;

3. locating the sector psychiatric teams in the community and not in the psychiatric hospital;

4. providing sufficient community services of a high level, particularly day care, mental health consultations, crisis intervention, and specialist out-patient clinics;

5. providing a range of community residential facilities such as houses, hostels and boarding-out;

6. providing support for the families of the mentally ill as outlined in paragraphs 3.6 to 3.10;

7. obtaining the community's acceptance and support for its handicapped and disadvantaged members.

3.13.   Orienting services towards community care applies not only to the mentally ill but also to the elderly and the mentally or physically handicapped. This may provide an opportunity for sharing services by different categories of patient, making it possible to develop a local service which might not be justified on the numbers of mentally ill alone.

3.14 Recommendations

1. **The psychiatric service should be community-oriented i.e. it should enable people to avail of a full range of services while continuing to live in their own homes (para.s 3.1 to 3.5).**

2. **The psychiatric team should support the families of patients living at home and provide active family therapy as required (para.s 3.7 to 3.9). In this regard, particular attention should be paid to the points set out in para. 3.10.**

3. **A variety of community-based services should be built up in accordance with the guidelines set out in para. 3.12.**

Chapter 4

Sectorisation

Definition

4.1 The term "sectorisation" is used to describe the process of providing a comprehensive psychiatric service for a population of known size normally resident within a clearly defined district. This service is provided by a multi-disciplinary psychiatric team with a consultant psychiatrist as its leader. It is important the this team sees its responsibilities as encompassing the sector as a whole and not simply the psychiatric hospital or unit which may be located within that sector. Under this arrangement, each team is responsible for all the psychiatric services of its sector and runs all out-patient clinics, day care and residential facilities. This form of organisation means that there are no barriers between the hospital and the community services. For example, psychiatric nursing is not regarded as something which happens only within the hospital; psychiatric nurses form part of the team and they work in the hospital or in the community according to the needs of the sector. We agree with the recommendation in the Report of the Review Group on the Community Psychiatric Nursing Service[1] that it will be necessary to train nurses who will operate with equal facility in in-patient, out-patient and day care facilities and that this will require a common basic grade throughout the service i.e. a unified nursing structure.

Sector Size

4.2 The special organisational needs of the psychiatric service have been recognised in different ways in different areas and some health boards have developed prototypes for sectors. Health boards tend to base their description of these services on the concept of the "catchment area" which is the accepted term used to describe the area served by a hospital.

4.3 In the Eastern Health Board area there are eight catchment areas:

Catchment Area	Population (1981)
Dublin North West	125,000
Dublin North Central	133,000
Dublin South East	85,000
Dublin North East	187,000
Dublin West and Kildare North	263,000
Dublin South Central	86,000
Dún Laoghaire and South East Dublin Co.	155,000
Wicklow	87,000

4.4 In the North-Eastern Health Board area a sectorisation plan based on four sectors, with a population of about 25,000 in each sector, has been in operation for a number of years in Counties Cavan and Monaghan and has worked very well. With populations of this size it is possible for the team to know the sector and the families who live in it and to develop good relationships with general practitioners and other health workers.

4.5 A somewhat different approach to sectorisation has been adopted in County Cork. Sectorised services were introduced in Cork in 1971 with four areas varying from 45,000 to 150,000 population. Units of this size permit a certain amount of specialisation. These units now coincide with the Community Care areas i.e. the administrative areas for the delivery of health services under the community care programme. Each unit is served by a team of consultant psychiatrists and other mental health personnel. It is reported that this model is operating successfully in Cork and this demonstrates that it is possible to run services with larger units of population. It has been argued that, while small sectors are suitable for rural areas, larger sectors are more practical in an urban setting where the population is more concentrated and where travelling does not present such a problem.

4.6 In principle, we favour the organisation of services for sectors of 25,000 to 30,000 population but we acknowledge that in some areas, particularly densely populated urban areas, it may be decided to develop sectors of larger size. There is a need for flexibility in this regard so that particular local circumstances can be taken into account. The designation of areas as sectors will be influenced by the population density and demographic characteristics, by public transport networks and by the degree of urbanisation.

Specialised Services

4.7 While small sectors are suitable for general psychiatry, there are some specialised services which can serve larger populations and which must therefore be developed to serve more than one sector. These include services for the elderly mentally infirm, certain high intensity rehabilitation programmes for chronic patients, child and adolescent psychiatry and small secure units for highly disturbed patients.

Sector Services

4.8   One of the main tasks of the psychiatric team, initially, will be to build up a range of community services in its area. These include day facilities, outpatient clinics, community residential accommodation and rehabilitation services as outlined in later chapters. In sectors of 25,000 to 30,000 population it will not always be possible to provide all of these services. For example, day facilities or sheltered workshops may need to be shared by more than one sector. The psychiatric team should be based in the sector so that there is a recognised centre to which people may be referred by their general practitioners. The organisation of services in each sector and the location of the headquarters for the psychiatric team are matters which will need to be planned at a local level. The norms for the provision of community services which are recommended in this report will be of assistance to local planners in carrying out this task.

4.9   Each sector should have access to hospital in-patient facilities as near as possible to the sector population. The in-patient service should consist of a psychiatric hospital or general hospital psychiatric unit serving a number of sectors, with responsibility for the in-patient psychiatric needs of these sectors. We use the term "catchment area" to describe collectively the sectors served by a psychiatric hospital or unit. At a later stage, as discussed in Chapter 7, in-patient facilities for a catchment area should include community-based units for new long-stay patients. The psychiatrists who are the leaders of the sectoral teams will also be on the staff of the hospital concerned. Each psychiatrist should develop a special interest in a specialised service. For example, in a hospital catchment area (comprising a number of sectors) one psychiatrist, in charge of a comprehensive service for a particular sector, might also take a special interest in the care of elderly persons with psychiatric problems. He would provide a consultant service on special problems associated with the elderly for other psychiatrists in that catchment area. Similarly, another psychiatrist in the catchment area might have a special interest in alcoholism or in rehabilitation programmes for chronic patients. Some specialised services such as child and adolescent psychiatry and small secure units for highly disturbed patients will serve more than one catchment area.

4.10   It is important that the sector team knows and understands the district in which it operates, the resident population of the district and their problems and needs. Satisfactory working relationships, including regular meetings and exchange of ideas, should exist with general practitioners and other health and community workers in the area. The sector team should also co-operate with and assist the families of patients and voluntary organisations concerned with the welfare of the mentally ill. This approach is essential in order to develop the type of comprehensive community-oriented psychiatric service we have outlined and is described in more detail in Chapter 5.

Designation of Sectors

4.11 We recommend that sectors for the delivery of the psychiatric service should, as far as practicable, share the same boundaries as the existing community care areas. This means that a community care area would usually incorporate a number of psychiatric sectors. Each health board should now take steps to:

—designate sectors;

—appoint a team with responsibility for each sector;

—decide on the in-patient facility, which will serve each sector.

4.12   In some areas, where the hospital catchment areas are coterminous with the community care areas and where services are already organised on sectorised lines, these measures will mean little or no change. In other areas these changes will be more difficult to implement, particularly in the case of health boards which now provide in-patient services for patients from other health boards. We recognise that there will be a need for some flexibility in these arrangements to meet local circumstances and to make best use of the facilities and personnel which are now available.

4.13   **Recommendations**

1. **The psychiatric service should be organised on the basis of sectorisation. This means that a psychiatric team should provide a comprehensive service to the population living in a particular district or sector (para. 4.1).**

2. **We favour the organisation of psychiatric services for sectors of 25,000 — 30,000 population where possible but we recognise that sectors of larger size may be necessary in densely populated areas (para. 4.6).**

19

3. A number of more specialised services which can serve larger populations should be developed for more than one sector (para. 4.7).

4. The psychiatric team should, where possible, be based in the sector (para. 4.8).

5. Each sector should have access to hospital in-patient facilities. This might be a psychiatric hospital or a general hospital psychiatric unit and it will serve a number of sectors forming one catchment area (para. 4.9).

6. Sectors for the delivery of psychiatric services should, as far as practicable, share the same boundaries as the existing community care areas (para. 4.11).

7. Each health board should now take steps to:

   —designate sectors;

   —appoint a team with responsibility for each sector;

   —decide on the in-patient facility, which will serve each sector (para. 4.11).

Chapter 5

Primary Health Care of Psychiatric Illness

Definition

5.1   Primary care of psychiatric patients is care provided by general pracitioners and associated community-based personnel. All persons with psychiatric problems who seek help from their family doctor come within the scope of primary care. The service provided to the mentally ill by public health nurses, social workers and others in the community health services and the major contribution provided by voluntary support groups are also essential aspects of primary care.

Extent of Mental Illness Treated by General Practitioners

5.2   The results of various studies show that general practitioners are presented with and treat the largest proportion of psychiatric morbidity among the population, leaving only a small and atypical proportion to the specialised psychiatric services.[1,2] The British White Paper "Better Services for the Mentally Ill" states:

> "General Practitioners working with other primary care staff at present undertake the medical treatment of nearly 90 per cent of diagnosed mental illness and it seems unlikely that this pattern of care will change significantly".[3]

A number of factors help to explain this situation:

1. it is accepted practice in this country for people to go to their family doctor when they feel something is wrong with them;

2. many mentally ill patients who seek medical assistance present with physical, rather than psychological, symptoms and the general practitioner is their obvious source of care;

3. there is still a reluctance on the part of many persons to admit that they need specialised psychiatric help;

4. many psychiatric disorders are associated with the patient's family background with which the general practitioner may be familiar;

5. many psychiatric disorders are long-term and the general practitioner may be in the best position to give continuing care and to be on hand in the event of a relapse;

6. many psychiatric illnesses may not be recognised by general practitioners and they may delay too long in referring patients for specialist advice.

It is a reasonable assumption that in Ireland, as well as in other countries, the general practitioner is the first medical contact for almost all patients who come to psychiatric care.

5.3   A large part of general practitioners' working time is spent dealing with psychiatric problems. Surveys of psychiatric illness among patients attending general practitioners in both England and the United States have shown very great variation between individual doctors in the rates which they report for psychiatric illness. From the United States it is reported that approximately 15% of patients presenting to general practitioners may be diagnosed as having a psychiatric or emotional disorder.[4, 5] Studies in the United Kingdom have found that between one-quarter and one-third of all illness treated by general practitioners fall into the category of mental disorder.[6] Shepherd et al. have reported:

> "Of some 15,000 patients at risk during a twelve-month period, rather more than 2,000, approximately 14%, consulted their doctor at least once for a condition diagnosed as entirely or largely psychiatric in nature. The bulk of these patients would be classifiable in the International Classification of Diseases as suffering from neurotic or personality disorders which therefore take their place among the commoner conditions in general practice".[2]

5.4   Such research findings are not yet available for Ireland. A sample of drugs prescribed in the General Medical Services (August, 1981) indicated that psychotropic drugs accounted for 13.5% of all drugs prescribed and for 9.8% of the total cost. A study of psychotropic drug prescribing by thirty general practitioners in West Cork[7] found that the prescribing rate for the doctors in this study was lower than in comparable studies in the United Kingdom and Belgium. The mean rate of prescribing found in this study (112 psychotropic drug prescriptions per 1,000 consultations) was also lower than that of the population covered by the General Medical Services (247 psychotropic drug prescriptions per 1,000 consultations in 1981).

22

Identification

5.5   A problem facing the general practitioner is that of recognising that a patient is suffering from a psychiatric disorder. Research studies have shown that general practitioners fail to identify about one third of the psychiatric morbidity that presents to them.[6, 8] This is due in part to the doctor's personality and interviewing style[6] and in part to the way in which the patient presents the problem. Goldberg and Blackwell[8] showed that the bulk of the hidden or missed psychiatric morbidity was in patients who, for various reasons, presented their emotional distress in physical terms.

Referral

5.6   There is evidence that only a small proportion of the psychiatric problems which present at general practitioner level are referred for specialist psychiatric care and that those who are referred tend to be retained under the psychiatrist's care.[2] There is very little transfer of patients in either direction between psychiatrists and general practitioners. Good patient care is seriously restricted by this lack of referral and movement. One explanation for the low rate of referral may be that general practitioners are successful in treating patients with a wide range of psychiatric conditions. It has been suggested that purely clinical features are also important in the selective referral of depressed patients from general practice.[9] Another reason for the low rate of referral probably relates to a reluctance on the part of patients and doctors to accept openly the existence of a psychiatric problem and the need for specialised psychiatric treatment.[2] Prejudices among both the general public and the medical profession may create barriers to appropriate care being provided for persons who are being treated at primary care level and who are suffering from psychoneurosis and psychosomatic disorders.

5.7   The second aspect of this question is that psychiatrists tend to retain patients who are referred to them. Data from the Three County Case Register operated by the Medico-Social Research Board show a low rate of referral by general practioners of patients to the psychiatric service and that, once patients come into the network of psychiatric services, they tend to remain there for a long time.[10] It is unlikely that psychiatrists differ greatly from their consultant colleagues in this respect. In most cases, it should be possible for the psychiatrist, having arranged whatever investigations are necessary for diagnosis and having recommended an appropriate course of treatment and management, to leave the continuing care and treatment of the patient in the hands of the general practitioner.

5.8   There is a need to improve communication and co-operation between general practitioners and psychiatrists. A review of the general practitioner's contribution to mental health care in Europe conducted by the World Health Organisation in 1973 led to agreement that:

> "The crucial question is not how the general practitioner can fit into the mental health services but rather how the psychiatrist can collaborate most effectively with primary care medical services and reinforce the effectiveness of the primary physician as a member of the mental health team".[11]

This underlines the key role of the general practitioner in the treatment of mental illness.

Treatment of Psychiatric Disorders by General Practitioners

5.9   Information about the nature of mental illness treated by general practitioners and also about the methods of treatment used in this country is lacking. Surveys from abroad of data from general practitioners give a very different picture of mental disorder from that suggested by hospital statistics. It has been found, for example, that psychotic illnesses comprise only a very small fraction of the total.[11] It appears that the great bulk of the general practitioner's psychiatric work-load consists of mixed anxiety/depressive states.

5.10   We consider that the amount of psychotropic drugs being prescribed by general practitioners, as shown in the prescribing habits under the General Medical Service, gives cause for concern. First, there is the problem of creating drug dependence. Secondly, because most of the problems presenting to the general practitioner are psychoneurotic or psychosmatic, they require the more elaborate kinds of diagnosis and management, including psychotherapy. It is important that the general practitioner tries to understand the psychology of the mentally ill patient and helps the patient deal with the underlying problem without undue reliance on drug therapy.

5.11   Therapy such as counselling and psychotherapy are time-consuming and it seems that the fee-per-item of service system in the General Medical Service is not conducive to these treatment methods. Indeed, we feel that this method of payment encourages high levels of visiting and prescribing by the doctor which may be both unnecessary and harmful and that both the low referral rate by general practitioners and the high prescribing of psychoactive drugs may be at least partially explained by the fee-per-item system in the General Medical Service. Insofar as good psychiatric care is concerned, there is a strong case for having an alternative method of payment which would encourage general practitioners to treat more patients using psychotherapy and counselling. We recommend that serious consideration be given to devising such a system.

24

5.12 The recent Report of the Working Party on the General Medical Service[12] also considered that the fee-per-item of service system may inhibit appropriate referral to, and collaboration with, other health care staff. The Working Party concluded that a system of payment which contains a strong element of reward for doctor patient contact is desirable and that rewards should be more responsive to the quality, rather than the quantity of doctors' services. This point was elaborated as follows:

> "This implies the capacity to differentiate between practices which vary in their ability to respond to the whole range of patients' needs, while removing the need for doctors to provide high volume of service when fewer but longer consultations with greater emphasis on education, reassurance and counselling, and less emphasis on the prescribing of medicines may be more appropriate".

We consider that a method of payment which would achieve the latter objective would be highly desirable and we welcome the recommendation of the Working Party concerning the option of a modified fee-per-service.

Under-Graduate Medical Education in Psychiatry

5.13 The modern medical student is introduced to the concept of psychological illness by formal lectures during the pre-clinical years. The under-graduate then receives practical experience in clinical psychiatry in the final years of training before qualification. This training includes a period of assignment to a psychiatric teaching unit, during which experience is gained in diagnosis and management of psychiatric disorders.

5.14 We recommend that the under-graduate's experience in the practice of clinical psychiatry should include assignment to a community psychiatric service. The student should have an opportunity to observe and participate in the work of day care facilities, specialist out-patient clinics, rehabilitation services and of community residential facilities for persons with psychiatric disability. Opportunities should be provided to accompany medical and nursing staff on home visits to patients and their families. Increased experience in child and adolescent psychiatry should also form part of the under-graduate curriculum. The most important element in the student's course should be supervised training in dealing with psychiatric problems likely to arise commonly in general practice with particular emphasis on the psycho-therapeutic approach.

Post-Graduate Training in Psychiatry

5.15 We feel that the present training schemes for medical graduates planning a career in general practice are not geared towards the more recent developments in psychiatric treatment methods and that in particular they do not prepare students adequately for the treatments required for psychoneurotic problems. Existing training is largely confined to acquiring experience in working in the traditional psychiatric hospital ward and trainee general practitioners do not receive sufficient out-patient experience. There is evidence that general practitioners feel some dissatisfaction with their present level of management skills and that they consider that their academic training has ill prepared them for managing patients' psychological problems.[13] The increasing development of vocational training programmes for medical graduates planning a career in general practice has meant that a small proportion of new entrants to general practice now receive a three to six month post-graduate training experience in psychiatry. At present in Ireland each of the three teaching centres, Cork, Dublin and Galway, has its own post-graduate day release training programme of lectures.

5.16   We recommend that post-graduate day release training in psychiatry for trainee general practitioners should be formalised along the following lines.

1. Trainee general practitioners should have six months experience of working with a sector team. During this six month period the trainee should receive formal teaching in the diagnosis and treatment of psychiatric illness as seen in general practice. In addition, he or she should have supervised clinical experience to develop skills in interviewing and supportive psychotherapy, with a particular emphasis on the management of neurotic disorders.

2. The trainee general practitioner should be trained in the use of community support facilities for the managment of psychiatric illness and gain a working knowledge of the role of a general practitioner in the case of the mentally ill in the community.

3. A diploma in clinical psychiatry should be awarded to medical practitioners who have satisfactorily completed a minimum of six months post-qualification experience in psychiatry.

4. Regular refresher courses in psychiatry should be available to general practitioners. These might be organised locally by the sector psychiatric service at regular intervals. The increasing involvement of consultant psychiatrists in domiciliary visits, carried out jointly with the patient's general practitioner, will provide an excellent opportunity for a valuable exchange of information; and the development of a much closer working relationship between the general practitioner and the local psychiatric service.

Promotion of Links Between Psychiatrists and General Practitioners

5.17   To ensure a comprehensive psychiatric service, there should be close communication between the members of the psychiatric team and the general practitioners in the team's area. The general practitioner can give valuable information to the psychiatrist about the history and home conditions of the patient. In the event of a patient being referred to the specialist psychiatric services, the psychiatrist can feed information back to the general practitioner about the patient's treatment and progress and discuss his or her future management. The organisation of services on a sectorised basis facilitates good links with the local general practitioners and with social workers and public health nurses. To formalise the links between the psychiatric team and other health care workers in the community we recommend that each team should provide mental health consultations (see para. 5.18 to 5.20) as part of its service.

Mental Health Consultation

5.18   The burden of mental illness is too great to be treated solely by mental health professionals even if the economic resources were made available. Mental health consultations, which first developed in the United States, involve trained mental health professionals working directly with general practitioners, nurses, social workers, school teachers and voluntary groups such as Samaritans, Simon Community, Alcoholics Anonymous. In this way, mental health professionals help these care givers cope with people with psychiatric problems. The World Health Organisation has strongly recommended in more than one report[11, 14] that mental health consultations should be part of the normal work of psychiatrists, that this should be openly recognised and formally included in the terms of appointment of psychiatrists and that the onus for setting up mental health consultations should rest with the psychiatric team.

5.19   In addition to better communication between psychiatrists and general practitioners, there is a need for increased co-operation between the psychiatric team and the community care service. In view of the major contribution of social workers, public health nurses and other professionals to primary care of the mentally ill, it is essential that each sector team should form effective working links with these personnel. Many psychiatric problems first come to the notice of the community care team. The establishment of good links between the psychiatric services and the community care services will ensure that the patient receives appropriate help quickly. For its part, the psychiatric team should be aware of the services, such as meals-on-wheels and home helps, provided under the community care programme and which would benefit their patients.

5.20   We recommend that the psychiatric team, as part of a comprehensive psychiatric service, should provide mental health consultations for general practitioners and for community care personnel. The team should also organise meetings and seminars to exchange information and experience with key personnel in the community such as teachers, clergy, Gardai and personnel managers. The primary objective of this two-way exchange would be to enable these key personnel to deal more effectively with the mental health problems of people with whom they come in contact and to inform them about the availability of the specialised psychiatric services. In addition, this process would help the sector team identify areas of need and treatment opportunities locally.

Crisis Intervention

5.21   Some hospital admissions are the product of acute social crisis. Crisis intervention services have been developed in many countries to reduce or prevent unnecessary admission to hospital after such crises. The objective of crisis intervention is to have the person seen quickly, the problem identified and help provided without moving the person from his or her usual environment. When a person must be removed from home he or she is normally taken to a crisis intervention unit which has a small number of beds and day places. The patient's stay in the unit is usually less than twenty-four hours. During this time the patient is fully assessed and a decision made on continuing treatment and care.

5.22   A crisis intervention service provides access to expert psychiatric help on a 24-hour basis without having to admit a person to hospital. This service is an important support facility for general practitioners and other primary care workers in enabling them to cope with critical situations while retaining responsibility for persons with psychiatric problems. A recent World Health Organisation Report[15] describes fifteen crisis intervention units in eight European countries. This investigation found that a crisis intervention service can produce a significant fall in psychiatric hospital admissions. Because of the rapid turnover of patients referred to the crisis intervention unit, a surprisingly small number of beds and day places was adequate for a large workload. It was also shown that a crisis intervention service can be established by diverting resources from existing services and that special buildings or other resources are not required.

5.23   The main components of a crisis intervention service may be summarised as:

1. expert psychiatric intervention on a 24-hour basis that is readily available, should a crisis or emergency arise;

2. access to a small number of beds so that the patient may be brought in for overnight care and assessment if required.

5.24   We consider that a crisis intervention service should be available to every sector. An emergency facility providing care and assistance is an important support for the families of patients living at home. In addition, it is to be expected that the crisis intervention service will be utilised by people with psycho-social problems, that is people under stress due to unexpected bereavement, breakdown of marriage, unexpected loss of employment or some other adverse life event. One crisis intervention facility might serve a number of sectors. It might operate from a day facility or from a supervised hostel or from a combination of these and should be located centrally in a catchment area. We wish to acknowledge the important contribution made by voluntary organisations such as the Samaritans and the Simon Community in providing emergency services for the mentally ill and other vulnerable groups in various parts of the country.

Domiciliary Consultations

5.25   Domiciliary consultations are carried out in some parts of the country at present. We consider that the practice of domiciliary consultations by members of the sector teams is an important component of an emergency service and that it can prevent unnecessary admissions to hospital. The availability of a psychiatrist or other member of the sector team to visit a patient at home is an important asset to the general practitioner. We consider that domiciliary visiting is particularly useful in the assessment of elderly patients with psychiatric illness and for all patients in isolated areas of the country where one might have to travel a long distance to attend a psychiatric facility. We recommend that domiciliary visiting should be recognised as part of the general responsibilities of the sector team.

5.26   **Recommendations**

1. **The sector psychiatric team should recognise the central role of general practitioners in the prevention and treatment of mental illness and should try to improve communication and co-operation with them (para. 5.2, 5.3 and 5.8).**

2. **In the case of patients who are referred for specialist treatment by general practitioners, the psychiatrist should provide consultation and specialist treatment as required and refer the patient**

back to the family doctor for continuing care and treatment as soon as this is possible. (para. 5.7).

3. The method of payment of general practitioners should be reviewed so that they are encouraged to spent sufficient time in treating patients with psychoneurotic disorders (para. 5.11).

4. Training of medical students and general practitioners should be revised in accordance with the recommendations made in para.s 5.13 to 5.16.

5. Psychiatrists and other members of the psychiatric team should provide mental health consultation for general practitioners and other community workers (para.s 5.17 to 5.20).

6. A crisis intervention service should be available to every sector (para.s 5.21 to 5.24).

7. Each sector team should provide a domiciliary consultation service if required. (para. 5.25).

Chapter 6

Day Care

Introduction

6.1   At present there are some 1,200 places available in about 40 day facilities for the mentally ill in this country. These day facilities vary in type and size. They play an important part in extending the range of care and treatment services available to persons suffering from mental illness. Day facilities are an essential component of the comprehensive, community-oriented psychiatric service which we favour. We recommend that there should be an increase in the number of day facilities so that more patients can be treated as day-patients rather than as in-patients. We consider that this approach is both clinically and economically justifiable and that it is what the people availing of the psychiatric service want for themselves.

6.2   In addition to an expansion in the number of psychiatric day facilities we consider that there should be greater co-operation between the psychiatric team and community care personnel. We have already recommended that the sector psychiatric team should develop close links with general practitioners, community care personnel and voluntary groups. Community care and voluntary care facilities will be available in this way to psychiatric patients.

Objective of Day Care

6.3   The objective of psychiatric day care is the provision of treatment and care, of an appropriate kind and in the required amount and frequency, for the mentally ill person without admission to hospital. Such care is provided in day care centres or in day hospitals. Patient care at a day facility may include a planned treatment programme on an individual or group basis as appropriate.

Day Care Services

6.4   The range of services appropriate to day care includes:

Assessment and diagnosis

Medication

Psychotherapy including behaviour therapy

Individual and group psychotherapy and family therapy

Occupational therapy

Social support and care (e.g. instruction and encouragement in social skills; provision of meals; support for the patient's family)

Instruction and recreation activities including light industrial therapy

Miscellaneous specialised services

The actual services provided in a particular day facility should be chosen to meet the known needs of the area it serves. Specialist out-patient clinics might also be held at the day facility. Every person attending at a day facility should be regularly assessed to ensure that services of maximum therapeutic value are being provided for that person and to check whether or not continued attendance at the day facility is necessary.

Present Provision of Day Facilities

6.5   The present provision of day facilities is shown in Table 6.1.

TABLE 6.1

Number of day facilities in December 1983 by health board area and number of places per 100,000 population (1981 Census of population)

Health Board Area	Number of Day Centres/Day Hospitals	Number of places	No. of places per 100,000 population
Eastern	20	784	65.6
Midland	—	—	—
Mid-Western	1	14	4.5
North-Eastern	4	102	35.3
North-Western[a]	2	35	16.8
South-Eastern	1	40	10.7
Southern	3	93	17.7
Western	8	112	32.8
TOTAL	39	1,180	34.3

Source: Department of Health.

[a]The North-Western Health Board operates a further 11 day hospitals providing some 179 places for geriatric, physically handicapped, socially handicapped and psychiatric patients. Less than 5% of these places are taken up by psychiatric patients.

It may be seen from this table that there is considerable variation in the availability of day facilities between health boards. While the Midland Health Board has no day facilities at present, a number are at the planning stage. New day facilities are being built or planned at present in 17 further locations throughout the country. The location of existing day facilities is given in Appendix 3.

Advantages of Day Care

6.6   The primary advantage of day care is that it allows patients to receive the treatment which they require while continuing to live in the community. Day care has also been shown to be cost-effective.[1] The Report of the Commission of Inquiry on Mental Illness[2] listed the following specific advantages of day care which are still valid today:

—avoids institutionalisation of the patient who requires long-term treatment;

—prevents the breakdown of home ties and associations with friends and colleagues;

—makes possible the treatment in the community of many patients who require more intensive therapy than can be provided at a weekly clinic;

—facilitates the earlier discharge of in-patients who can continue necessary treatment on a day basis;

—helps patients to re-adapt themselves to outside surroundings after a stay in hospital.

6.7   The day facility is a key element in the strategy of developing a community-oriented psychiatric service. It will make available psychiatric services for people in their own locality and without admission for in-patient treatment, as well as acting as a filter in order to ensure that only those in genuine need of in-patient services are admitted to hospital. It may also enable earlier discharge of those who must be admitted for in-patient treatment.

Persons who would benefit from day care

6.8   Day care is provided primarily for persons living in the community. They may live at home or in a residential facility such as a hostel. They may require day care for a short period or on a long-term basis. Patients discharged from in-patient psychiatric care may need to attend at a day facility for a limited period of time. Following this treatment, they may be able to transfer to a sheltered workshop or to a fully independent life in the community. Former long-stay patients of psychiatric hospitals who are moved to community residential accommodation may need to attend at a day facility on a more long-term basis. They will need a high degree of skilled medical and nursing attention. They can attend for required treatment during the day and return to the community residence at night. In addition, some patients with chronic mental illness will attend the day facility for social support. This group of patients might also attend at a day centre provided for other groups by the community care services. Such chronic patients include people with little employment potential in need of counselling and medication and who would also benefit from the occupational and recreational activities provided in day facilities. Some patients might attend the day facility one day a week while others might attend five days a week. In the case of mentally ill persons living at home, day facilities are an essential support service for relatives and enhance the patient's potential to make satisfactory progress.

Different Kinds of Day Care

6.9   The type of day care facility provided may be any one of a number of different kinds. Local circumstances and needs will determine the choice for each area. Four types of day facility are described here:

1. Day Hospital

2. Day Centre

3. Combined Day Facility

4. Mental Health Centre

Day Hospital

6.10   The function of the day hospital is to provide intensive treatment equivalent to that available in a hospital in-patient setting for acutely ill patients. This means that a comprehensive range of treatments will be provided. In addition, clinics can be held and a range of investigative procedures performed. The day hospital acts as the focus of psychiatric care in an area and is primarily for active treatment of patients with psychiatric disorders. The sector team should be based in the day hospital, if one is located in the sector.

Day Centre

6.11   The role of the psychiatric day centre is to provide social care for patients whose needs cannot be met at community care day centres. The day centre may also offer treatment. Rehabilitation and activation services may be provided and these could include occupational therapy, social skills training and light industrial therapy. Both day centres and day hospitals have a therapeutic role but, unlike day hospitals, the orientation of day centres is social. Each sector of 25,000-30,000 population might have its own day centre but this will depend on the needs of its population.

34

Combined Day Facility

6.12 While there is a clear distinction between the purpose of a day hospital and of a day centre, it is generally accepted that in practice there is a degree of overlap between the two facilities. Experience suggests that their functions tend to merge and that often what is set up as a day hospital gradually takes on the social role of a day centre. The National Day Care Project in the United Kingdom[3] found that the users of both facilities resembled each other in age, sex, marital status, living arrangements and in their perceptions of their own physical and mental health. A Department of Health and Social Security (London) discussion paper[4] has raised doubts about the need for separate day centres and day hospitals.

6.13 Whether a day centre service or a day hospital service or a service combining both should be provided in a particular area will depend on local needs and existing facilities. We consider that in certain circumstances it would be feasible to provide both types of service in one combined day facility. There is a danger, however, that some patients will become chronically dependent on the combined facility and some selectivity in the type of patient treated may be required so that expensive specialised services are not provided for patients whose primary need is for social care. A study in Birmingham suggested that day hospitals there had become filled up with long-term patients who had been discharged from psychiatric hospitals.[5]

Mental Health Centre

6.14 Day care may also be provided at a comprehensive mental health centre. The main features of a mental health centre are as follows:

1. it acts as the centre of the psychiatric service in a sector and the sector team has its headquarters there;

2. it provides an active treatment service similar to a day hospital but also includes a small number of twenty-four hour care beds for assessment and crisis intervention purposes; these beds may be in the mental health centre itself or in a house or supervised hostel nearby;

3. it provides services similar to those available in a day centre;

4. it contains facilities for out-patient consultations;

5. it provides a base for mental health consultations with general practitioners, community care personnel and other key figures in the local community;

6. it may be used by the psychiatric team or by voluntary groups to

provide social activities for patients in the evening or for general educational purposes.

The mental health centre offers both day hospital and day care facilities but has a wider remit than the combined facility described in paragraphs 6.12 and 6.13. The in-patient component should be small, perhaps of the order of 0.1 places per 1,000 population. This accommodation should be managed as lodgings and used for such purposes as overnight assessment and for crisis intervention. These beds may replace or limit the need for traditional, in-patient hospital care, as has been demonstrated in Trieste, Italy.[6] The development of a comprehensive mental health centre is a particularly suitable method of moving towards a more community-oriented psychiatric service.

Number of Places

6.15 Every psychiatric sector should have access to a day facility. Some sectors will have their own day centre whereas a day hospital or mental health centre may be shared by a number of sectors. The day facility should be well served by public transport. In city areas centres should be on a district bus or train route. There is insufficient experience of psychiatric day services in this country to make a firm estimate of the number of places required to be made. The British guidelines for the number of places required are 0.3 day hospital places and 0.6 day centre places per 1,000 population.[7] In the interest of having a single guideline, we suggest that a target of 0.75 day places per 1,000 population be the immediate aim. This provision might include several different types of day facilities but it can be expected that the greater demand will be on day centre type services i.e. social care. It may be necessary to increase this allocation when more experience is gained of the operation of day facilities. We consider that the target of 0.75 places per 1,000 population should be formally evaluated when the number of places available approaches the 0.5 mark. Some areas have already reached this level and the need for additional places should be evaluated now. We recommend that the catchment area management committee referred to in Chapter 14 should undertake this evaluation.

6.16 We suggest that the number of places in a day centre should be limited to about 25. The number of persons to be catered for in other types of day facility should be worked out locally with reference to the population being served and the level of services being provided.

Payment of Disabled Persons Maintenance Allowance (D.P.M.A.) at the Day Care Facility

6.17 Some mentally ill patients living in the community tend to remain inactive during the day. It would be helpful if patients could be motivated to attend a day facility so that the dangers of social isolation and withdrawal can be reduced. We noted that in Camberwell, London a weekly allowance is paid for attendance at a day centre for occupational therapy.[8] We consider that the D.P.M.A. could be used as an effective means of encouraging patients to visit the local day facility. Arrangements should be made to pay out the D.P.M.A. to patients entitled to receive it at psychiatric day facilities. The psychiatric nurse would then be in a position to motivate those patients who are reluctant to attend the day centre. However, non-attendance should not result in the allowance not being paid.

Centres for Mixed Categories of Patients

6.18   We examined the question of mentally ill persons attending the same day facility as persons with other handicaps such as the mentally and physically handicapped. Arrangements of this kind are operating to a certain extent in the field of work training. People with mixed handicaps attend the same workshops and the experience to date suggests that these workshops are working reasonably well. Sharing of day centres has also occurred in areas remote from psychiatric hospitals and the needs of many mentally ill patients can be met by attendance at general day centres. However, we consider that mentally ill patients with more severe disability should attend centres catering solely for the mentally ill. It will be the responsibility of each sector team to decide when general day centres might be used by an individual patient and when attendance at a psychiatric day facility would be more appropriate.

Need for Evaluation

6.19   In drawing up recommendations on psychiatric day facilities, we were conscious of the limited experience and absence of evaluation of the operation of day facilities in this country to date. The availability of effective day care is a pre-requisite to achieving the type of psychiatric service we describe in this report. Research suggests that day care needs to be well planned, structured and interlinked with the other components of a comprehensive psychiatric service.[9] In view of the importance of day care, we recommend that there should be continuous evaluation of existing and new day facilities. A recent review of day care for patients with psychiatric disorders states that clinicians and research workers should place more emphasis on the individual assessment and treatment of patients and on the reliable and valid measurement of therapeutic outcome.[10]

6.20   We consider that the following pointers should be used in evaluating day facilities:

—Has the day facility a firm objective in terms of the service it aims to provide? Is it carrying out this function?

—Are certain types of occupational activities more therapeutic than others?

—Has the day facility established links with other psychiatric services in the area and with community care and general practitioner services?

—Are the specific needs of the population being met adequately, taking account of age-structure and other relevant factors? Could some patients attending the psychiatric day facility attend at a day facility provided by the community care service for other groups?

We recommend that this process of evaluation should be carried out by the sector teams providing services at the day facilities in association with the catchment area management committee.

6.21 Recommendations

1. **There should be increased development of day facilities (para. 6.1).**

2. **The psychiatric team should avail of community care and voluntary care facilities for psychiatric patients where appropriate (para. 6.2 and 6.18).**

3. **A number of different types of day facility is feasible. Each local service should decide which model would best suit the needs of its area (para.s 6.9 to 6.14).**

4. **The planning guideline for day facilities should be set at 0.75 day places per 1,000 population. When the number of day places approaches the 0.5 mark, the ratio should be reviewed (para. 6.15).**

5. **The D.P.M.A. should be paid out at the day facility in order to encourage attendance (para. 6.17).**

6. **There should be continuous evaluation of existing and new day facilities. This evaluation should be carried out by the appropriate sector teams in association with the catchment area management committee (para. 6.19 and 6.20).**

Chapter 7

Hospital In-Patient Services

Present In-Patient Services

7.1 Psychiatric in-patient services in this country are provided mainly in psychiatric hospitals and to a lesser extent in the psychiatric units in ten general hospitals. On 31 December, 1983 there were 12,802 patients, including mentally handicapped patients, resident in all psychiatric hospitals and units.[1] The distribution of these patients by type of hospital is shown in Table 7.1.

TABLE 7.1

Distribution of patients in residence in Irish psychiatric hospitals and units on 31 December, 1983 by type of facility

Type of Hospital	Number of Patients
Health Board Psychiatric Hospitals	11,582
Private Psychiatric Hospitals	896
General Hospital Psychiatric Units	324
Total	12,802

7.2 The total number of patients resident in psychiatric hospitals and units has declined steadily in the past twenty years. In 1963 the total number of such patients was 19,801.[2] By 1971 it had declined to 16,661[3] and by the end of 1983 it was down to 12,802. The 1981 census of psychiatric hospitals and units recorded that 2,170 patients, or 15.5% of the total number in residence, were mentally handicapped.[4] Excluding these mentally handicapped patients, the census showed that about 72% of psychiatric in-patients in 1981 had been in hospital for over a year; 39% were aged over 65; and schizophrenia was the largest diagnostic category, accounting for 52% of all psychiatric patients.

The Psychiatric Hospitals

7.3 There are 22 health board psychiatric hospitals and 15 private psychiatric hospitals in the State. Some of the beds in the private psychiatric hospitals are used by public patients by arrangement with health boards. The outstanding feature of the psychiatric hospitals in recent years has been the persistent decline in the number of psychiatric beds in use. However, there are still many patients in these hospitals who, with proper training and rehabilitation, could be discharged to residential accommodation in the community. This means that there is still considerable scope for a further decline in the size of the patient population.

7.4   Side by side with the decline in the number of psychiatric beds, has been an upward trend in the number of admissions. The number of admissions, excluding mental handicap patients, to psychiatric hospitals increased from 18,738 in 1970[5] to 23,673 in 1982.[6] The number of discharges of such patients in 1982 was 23,542. These trends indicate a greater level of activity in the hospitals. The number of admissions has now stabilised and there is evidence that it is beginning to fall in some hospitals.

Psychiatric Units in General Hospitals

7.5   The general hospitals with psychiatric units are:

	Number of Beds
St. Vincent's Hospital, Elm Park, Dublin	28
St. James's Hospital, Dublin	50
Waterford Regional Hospital, Ardkeen	46
Letterkenny General Hospital	50
St. Joseph's Hospital, Clonmel	50
Cork Regional Hospital	50
Limerick Regional Hospital	46
Galway Regional Hospital	38
Castlebar General Hospital	44
District Hospital, Skibbereen	22
Total	424

7.6   It is proposed that new psychiatric units will be provided as part of the following new or extended general hospitals:

	Number of Beds	Stage of Development of psychiatric unit
Tralee General Hospital	50	built
Beaumont Hospital, Dublin	50	built
Cavan General Hospital	32	being built
Mater Hospital, Dublin	50	in planning
James Connolly Memorial Hospital, Blanchardstown	50	in planning
St. Luke's Hospital, Kilkenny	30	preliminary planning
Wexford General Hospital	44	preliminary planning
Tallaght Hospital, Dublin	50	preliminary planning
Naas County Hospital	30	preliminary planning
Total	386	

7.7   There were 4,699 admissions to general hospital units in 1982 which represented 16.6% of the total number of psychiatric admissions to psychiatric in-patient facilities.[6] Although the general hospital units account for less than 4% of psychiatric beds, they admit more than 16% of patients who require in-patient admission. Administratively, these units come under the general hospital programme but the psychiatrists and nursing staff are provided by the psychiatric services programme.

Admissions to Hospital

7.8   As pointed out in paragraph 7.4, the number of psychiatric hospital admissions has stabilised and there is some evidence that it is beginning to fall. With the continuing development of community-based facilities, which will take over much of the role previously filled by the hospital, there should be no further major increase in the number of hospital admissions. Indeed, the availability of treatment and support services in the community should lead to a continuing decline in the length of stay in hospital and a very significant reduction in the number of patients who remain in hospital for an indefinite period. Another relevant factor is that schizophrenia, which accounts for more patients resident in psychiatric hospitals than any other condition, is now recognised as an illness with reasonably good prospects for remission provided there is not the added disability of institutionalisation.[7] Many of the chronic disabilities of old long-stay schizophrenic patients are largely the result of their being inactive for many years.

7.9   In paragraphs 7.41 to 7.44 we set out the considerations which have led us to recommend that, ideally, the in-patient service for all admissions should be provided in psychiatric units in general hospitals. The in-patient facility in a comprehensive, sectorised service should cater for admissions from a designated catchment area. This area would consist of one or more psychiatric sectors and it may be decided to divide up the hospital accommodation between the various sectors. It is important that the in-patient service, whether this is a hospital or unit, should take all psychiatric patients from the sectors in its catchment area who need in-patient care. In particular, there should be no question of accepting only certain types of patients for admission such as those from the higher social classes or those with a good prognosis. There should be no exclusion of patients with chronic psychotic illness because their behaviour might be socially objectionable. The provision of treatment for all admissions in the one setting for a particular population is in line with the principle of a sectorised service. The same psychiatric team will provide support services and review the patient's progress after discharge from in-patient treatment so that continuity of patient care is ensured. It is worth recalling that the founders of sector psychiatry in their demonstration service in the 13th Arrondissement of Paris laid it down as a primary operational

41

principle that in-patient units should be mixed: mixed as to sex, mixed as to diagnostic category and mixed as to stage of illness.[8] Following these maxims, there should be one service for all admissions with regular assessment and review of each patient's progress, irrespective of the level of disability. In practice, this will require the integration of the sexes, both patients and staff.

7.10　On the assumption that a range of community support services will be available, the great majority of persons who are admitted to hospital will be discharged in a reasonably short time. For some, the period of hospital stay may, of necessity, extend to some months. It is to be expected that a small minority of these patients will continue to need fairly intensive supervision even after completing this extended stay in hospital. These are usually referred to as new long-stay patients and the needs of this group are examined in paragraphs 7.24 to 7.31.

Liaison Psychiatry

7.11　Liaison psychiatry is the term used to describe the operation of a psychiatric service for patients admitted to a general hospital with non-psychiatric conditions but who may have underlying psychiatric disorders. We consider that psychiatrists in general hospitals have an important role to play by providing consultation to their medical and surgical colleagues, as well as to the casualty services. A physical illness may well be complicated by a psychiatric disorder and vice versa. Liaison psychiatry has evolved during the past decade but its potential has not yet been fully explored in Ireland. We recommend that psychiatrists in psychiatric units in general hospitals should provide a liaison psychiatry service within the general hospital.

Patient Definition by Length of Stay

7.12　For convenience in calculating bed requirements, short-stay patients have been defined as patients with a length of stay of up to 3 months in hospital; medium-stay patients have been defined as patients with a length of stay of 3 to 12 months in hospital; long-stay patients are those whose stay in hospital exceeds 12 months.

Number of Beds Required for Short-Stay and Medium-Stay Patients (all ages)

7.13　In 1982 the number of discharges from psychiatric hospitals and units with a duration of stay of less than one year was about 27,000 of whom 25,000 had a stay of less than three months.[6] These figures include all age groups. If it is assumed:

42

1. that the number of short-stay admissions will be of the order of 25,000 a year,

2. that the average length of stay for these admissions will be 21 days,

3. that 85% bed occupancy is the norm, then the short stay bed requirement would work out at something less than 0.5 beds per 1,000 total population. Similarly, if it is assumed:

4. that the number of medium-stay admissions will be of the order of 2,000 a year,

5. that the average length of stay for these admissions will be 4 months,

6. that 90% bed occupancy is the norm, then the medium-stay bed requirement would work out at about 0.2 beds per 1,000 total population.

7.14   The Department of Health and Social Security (London) report "Better Services for the Mentally Ill"[9] put forward a guideline of 0.5 beds per 1,000 total population for short-stay and medium-stay patients as defined in paragraph 7.12. In a planning document prepared by that Department in 1981[10] the following estimates of bed requirements per 1,000 total population for the year 1991 were given:

	Short-Stay	Medium-Stay	Total
Under 65 years	0.243	0.038	0.281
Over 65 years	0.121	0.115	0.236
Total	0.364	0.153	0.517

In this estimate, the dividing line between short-stay and medium-stay is three months for persons over 65 years of age and six months for persons under 65. It was assumed that the trends in admission rates and duration of stay which had been observed up to 1978 would continue until 1984 and remain at the values obtained in that year. It was stated in the paper that these estimates probably exaggerated real requirements because of a number of statistical factors which could not adequately be allowed for. A more recent Department of Health and Social Security document, prepared in 1983, suggests that the correct level of provision for short-stay and medium-stay patients may lie somewhere between 0.3 and 0.5 beds per 1,000 population.[11]

7.15   In Sweden, where the policy is to transfer emergency and short-stay treatment in its entirety to general hospitals, bed requirements are estimated at 0.5 to 0.7 per 1,000 inhabitants.[12]

7.16   We consider that, as a more comprehensive type of psychiatric service starts to replace the existing institution-based service, these estimates of bed requirements will need to be revised downwards. We recommend accordingly that, at this stage, the planning guideline be put at 0.5 beds per 1,000 total population for short-stay and medium-stay patients combined. The actual division between the two categories of patients depends on a number of local circumstances and can be worked out locally as the need arises.

Long-Stay Patients

7.17   The present convention is to designate all persons who have been hospitalised continuously for one year or more as "long-stay" and to divide these into two groups. The first group consists of patients who were admitted before modern methods of treatment were introduced and who have spent many years in hospital. This group is called the old long-stay group. The other group consists of patients who were admitted to hospital in more recent times and who, despite advances in treatment and rehabilitation, have nevertheless become long-stay. These are referred to as the new long-stay patients.

Old Long-Stay Patients

7.18   Some of the old long-stay patients suffer from severe mentally or physically handicapping conditions and have little prospect of discharge from institutional care. On the other hand, some need not have been admitted to hospital in the first place and could be discharged either immediately or after a programme of social training and rehabilitation if alternative accommodation were available for them.

Number of Beds Required for Old Long-Stay Patients.

7.19   The number of beds needed in the future for old long-stay psychiatric patients will vary from one area to another and will depend on factors such as:

—the number of such patients now in hospital

—the potential for discharging patients to community residences and the success in achieving this

—the age and life expectancy of those patients who must remain in hospital.

7.20   An illustration of an approach to estimating the bed needs for old long-stay patients is available from work done by a project team in planning the future of St. Ita's Hospital, Portrane. The details are given in Appendix 4. We consider that a similar exercise should be undertaken in every psychiatric hospital. This will provide a firmer base for estimating the number of old long-stay patients in the hospital at different times in the future. Health boards should set up teams of appropriate personnel to do this work. Every project should include:

1. an assessment of patients in the hospital with particular reference to
   —age,
   —diagnosis,
   —current treatment programme,
   —mental and physical condition,
   —length of time in hospital,
   —home circumstances,
   —likelihood of discharge to community residence;

2. consideration of suitability of patients for transfer to geriatric care;

3. an estimate of the number of patients who, following a period of training and preparation, would be capable of living in the community;

4. an estimate of the number of long-stay patients who will be resident in the hospital at different times in the future. This can be done by applying expected mortality rates, such as those used in the Portrane project, to the patients who must remain in hospital.

7.21 It has been estimated that there are now about 8,400 old long-stay patients in residence in the psychiatric hospitals, many of whom are elderly. By applying expected mortality rates to their age distribution, it has been calculated that in 20 years time the old long-stay population will have been reduced by death to about 3,000. The estimated size of this group of patients at five-year intervals is as follows:—

Year	Number of Patients
1983	8,400
1988	6,800
1993	5,200
1998	4,000
2003	3,000

These projections are based on the long-stay patients who are now in hospital and they do not take account of any new long-stay patients. As stated already, it should be possible to discharge some of the old long-stay patients into residential accommodation in the community. Depending on the extent to which this occurs, the above projections, which show the decline in numbers by death only, will need to be reduced.

7.22   In the planning document prepared by the Department of Health and Social Security (London) in 1981,[10] it is noted that the number of long-stay patients is declining as a result of both discharges and deaths at a rate of about 10% per annum. It is presumed in that document that the decline will continue at a rate of between 9% and 12% per annum. If the 8,400 long-stay patients in Irish psychiatric hospitals were to decline at a rate of 12% per annum, their number would be reduced to 650 by the year 2003.

Rehabilitation of Old Long-Stay Patients

7.23   We consider that the potential for discharging old long-stay patients to community residences should be fully explored in all hospitals. This will require a careful assessment of patients and programmes of rehabilitation and social training as described in Chapter 10. These measures should be accompanied by the acquisition of suitable residential accommodation in the community as outlined in Chapter 9. We recognise that it will not be possible to rehabilitate all patients for independent living in the community. We consider that patients who cannot be rehabilitated to this extent should be allowed to spend their remaining years in the hospitals where they now live. They should continue to participate in rehabilitation programmes appropriate to their needs. In this way, any potential for improvement in these patients will be realised and the provision of active therapy for them will enhance their quality of life. As rehabilitation and training programmes begin to take effect, the numbers in residence will be reduced and overcrowding will be eliminated. The improvement schemes of the last three years have already made a significant contribution to upgrading the physical condition of many psychi-atric hospitals.

New Long-Stay Patients

7.24   Even though the pattern of service advocated in this report has a strong community orientation, we recognise that there will be a small number of patients who will need to remain in hospital. These new long-stay patients may be defined as those persons who, despite a full assessment, an active treatment and rehabilitation programme and the availability of a full range of community-oriented services, need the regular care and supervision normally provided for hospital in-patients. They include persons who are severly incapacitated as a result of a psychiatric illness such as severe schizophrenia and persons with a multiplicity of disabilities, which together make any independent form of living impracticable. They also include a small number of patients whose behaviour is socially unacceptable and who need to be retained in hospital for their own and society's good.

46

Location of In-patient Service for New Long-Stay Patients

7.25   New long-stay patients may be cared for in hospital where continuing efforts will be made to prepare them for discharge home or to a community residence. However, we consider that a busy general hospital is a poor social environment in which to live for a long time. There is a need to innovate and experiment with various models of care for new long-stay hospital patients. We are attracted by the potential of hostels providing a high level of support in caring for such patients. The hostel would be a special residence in the community providing, among other things, twenty-four hour nursing care. Such a residence might be associated with a hospital providing an in-patient psychiatric service, although it need not necessarily be located in close proximity to that hospital. The number of beds required would be relatively small. Since it would involve a transfer of service from psychiatric hospitals rather than the creation of a new service, the hostels should not require any extra staff posts. The nurses and domestic staff required should be recruited from among existing staff in the psychiatric service.

7.26   The high support hostel might best be located in a building capable of accommodating 15 to 20 patients, together with an appropriate number of places for nurses and other staff. Patients would receive care and support of a standard which is normally provided in hospital. One of its primary functions would be to prepare patients for discharge to a community residence with a lower level of support, such as a domestic scale residence or a flat where they can have a more independent life-style.

7.27   We wish to emphasise the importance of resisting the temptation to transfer new long-stay patients to accommodation occupied by old long-stay patients. This would perpetuate the chronic, long-stay aspect of the psychiatric hospitals and would have the following adverse effects:

1.   It would tend to exacerbate overcrowding in the psychiatric hospitals;

2.   It would inhibit efforts to establish better conditions and to provide more individual attention for the old long-stay patients, some of whom will spend the rest of their lives in the psychiatric hospitals;

3.   It would reduce considerably the impetus to provide intensive rehabilitation and regular review of the emerging new long-stay patients;

4.   It would deflect attention from the need to provide comprehensive community facilities.

47

Secure Accommodation

7.28   A very small number of patients will, at some time during their patient careers, display aggressive tendencies causing a need for secure accommodation — usually for a short time only. The number of persons for whom such provision is needed is extremely small and special secure units located at regional centres, say Dublin, Cork and Galway, should meet national requirements. We consider that a separate special study is needed to determine the size of the regional units and we recommend that such a study be carried out by representatives of the professional groups providing the psychiatric service.

Number of Beds Required for New Long-Stay Patients aged under 65 years.

7.29   In devising a planning guideline for the number of beds required for new long-stay patients aged less than 65 years, it is helpful to review the evidence on which to base a recommendation:

1. Data from St. Loman's Hospital, Dublin,[13] suggests that the number of beds required for new long-stay psychiatric patients aged under 65 years is of the order of 0.27 beds per 1,000 total population;

2. In St. Davnet's Hospital, Monaghan in the period 1973 to 1980 the accumulation of new long-stay psychiatric patients under 65 years of age required 0.28 beds per 1,000 total population;[14]

3. An assessment carried out on a sample of patients in St. Ita's Hospital, Portrane suggested that, with the development of a full range of community psychiatric services, the number of beds required for new long-stay patients aged under 65 years would correspond to 0.22 beds per 1,000 total population;

4. The Department of Health and Social Security (London) Report "Better Services for the Mentally Ill"[9] estimated the need for in-patient places for new long-stay patients under 65 years of age at 0.17 per 1,000 total population. This estimate was based on a study of a sample of patients under 65 years of age who had been in hospital for more than one year and less than three years and identifying those who needed 24 hour medical and nursing supervision. They were drawn predominantly from those suffering from chronic schizophrenia. In the 1981 Department of Health and Social Security planning document[10] the bed requirement in 1991 for new long-stay patients under 65 years of age was estimated at 0.23 beds per 1,000 total population.

48

7.30   Arising from our analysis of the available evidence and taking account of the expected development of a comprehensive, community-oriented psychiatric service, we recommend that the planning guideline for hospital places for new long-stay patients under 65 years of age be set at 0.2 beds per 1,000 total population. These might be located in a high support hostel as referred to in paragraph 7.25. Because of the tentative nature of this guideline and its dependence on the development of adequate community facilities, we accept that the actual ratio will vary somewhat from area to area. In particular, there may be a case for allowing for some extra provision for rural areas which are thinly populated.

Number of Beds required for New Long-Stay Patients aged 65 years or over

7.31   The question of planning services for elderly mentally infirm persons is considered in Chapter 11. In line with the general principles on which this report is based, we envisage the great majority of these persons being cared for in the community. However, there will be a small number who will need continuous care from the psychiatric service in a hospital-type setting. These will consist mainly of persons with severe forms of functional mental illness and persons who have severe dementia combined with severe behaviour disturbance. We recommend a provision of the order of 2.5 beds per 1,000 population aged 65 or over (or about 0.3 places per 1,000 total population) for these new long-stay patients aged 65 or over and we consider that these places should also be located in small, high support units in the community. The rationale behind these recommendations is outlined in Chapter 11.

Summary of Bed Requirements

7.32   In the preceding paragraphs we have considered the question of hospital bed requirements for short-stay and medium-stay patients, for old long-stay patients and new long-stay patients in the context of a well developed community-oriented, comprehensive psychiatric service. Our conclusions on the number of beds required per 1,000 total population are as follows:

	Short and Medium Stay Patients	New Long-Stay Patients	Old Long-Stay Patients
Under 65 years Over 65 years	0.5	0.2 0.3	Variable and Decreasing
Total	0.5	0.5	—

It is not possible to devise a standard ratio for the old long-stay patients which would apply in all areas. This must be worked out separately by each sector team. Guidelines for doing this are set out in paragraph 7.20.

7.33 We appreciate the very tentative nature of these hospital bed norms and the absence, at this stage, of sufficient experience to enable them to be more accurately measured. It is of the utmost importance, therefore, that the provision of in-patient facilities and their contribution to meeting the needs of psychiatric patients should be monitored closely as experience is gained in the operation of the service in the future.

7.34 There are two special categories of persons who occupy beds in psychiatric hospitals and to whom some reference must now be made. These are mentally handicapped persons and elderly persons.

Mentally Handicapped Patients

7.35 It has been the policy of the Department of Health for some years now not to admit any more mentally handicapped persons to psychiatric hospitals.[15] These hospitals are not suitable for the care of mentally handicapped persons, most of whom are not mentally ill. At the time of the 1981 Psychiatric Census, mentally handicapped persons resident in these hospitals numbered 2,170,[4] a reduction of 19% since the previous census in 1971. However, mentally handicapped patients as a proportion of all patients did not change in this ten-year period.

7.36 It is accepted that many of the mentally handicapped persons at present in psychiatric hospitals will continue to depend on the psychiatric services for care throughout their lives. Many of them are by now totally dependent on institutional care and have lost contact with family and friends. The general shortage of places for adults within the mental handicap service will also make it difficult to relocate any significant number of mentally handicapped residents from psychiatric hospitals.

7.37 We consider that a first essential step in the care of mentally handicapped persons who are in psychiatric hospitals is that they should be segregated from the mentally ill. It should be possible to have mentally handicapped persons accommodated in their own section of the hospital with programmes of care and activity which are suited to their needs. We consider that those in charge of the mental handicap service should liaise with the management of psychiatric hospitals in advising on appropriate programmes and facilities. The mental handicap service should assume responsibility for the segregated units when provided. It may then be possible to consider placing some of the residents in specialised community services with adequate back-up facilities. The question of whether or not more mentally handicapped patients should be admitted to these separate mental handicap facilities on the psychiatric hospital campus will depend on local circumstances and in particular on the general availability of mental handicap services in an area.

50

7.38   We consider that, whenever possible, disturbed mentally handicapped persons should be catered for within the special services for the mentally handicapped. The suggested liaison between psychiatric and mental handicap services referred to in the previous paragraph should facilitate this.

Elderly Patients

7.39   About 40% of existing long-stay patients in Irish psychiatric hospitals are over 65 years of age and over 40% of these are over 75 years of age.[4] These people are subject to the physical and mental infirmities associated with their age and the caring services provided by psychiatric nurses are of benefit to them. The majority of these old people have functional psychiatric problems and a change from the psychiatric to the geriatric service would not be advisable because of the harm which might be caused to individual patients by changing them from the living environment to which they have grown accustomed. Such a change would also be impracticable because the geriatric services would not be able to cope with this extra demand.

7.40   Where there is a large number of elderly persons in psychiatric hospitals whose needs are primarily geriatric, we consider that they should be accommodated in a part of the hospital which is specially set aside for them. Those responsible for the geriatric service should be involved in this re-organisation and in designing programmes of care for patients. It should be the aim that in time the geriatric service would take complete responsiblity for these patients.

Location of In-Patient Facilities for Admissions

7.41   We have given considerable thought to the question of where hospital admissions should be accommodated. We have concluded that all admissions should go to psychiatric units which are in, or closely associated with, general hospitals. This conclusion is strictly on the understanding that a hospital providing an in-patient service will do so for a designated catchment area (made up of one or more psychiatric sectors) and will take all psychiatric patients from this area in need of admission to hospital. The crisis intervention service with its twenty-four hour beds will supplement the in-patient service provided at the general hospital.

7.42   The provision of in-patient psychiatric services at general hospitals is accepted in most western countries and is an integral part of the World Health Organisation programme for comprehensive psychiatric services. The benefits which follow the implementation of this policy are compelling:

1. It brings to an end the isolation which has been so damaging to the concept and the practice of modern psychiatry;

2. It recognises psychiatry as a medical specialty to the advantage of both psychiatry and other areas of medical practice — in particular, it improves the treatment facilities in the many cases in which mental illness has a physical as well as a psychiatric basis;

3. It makes psychiatric treatment more acceptable to those who need it;

4. It increases the attractiveness of a career in psychiatry with consequential benefits in the recruitment of staff of a high calibre;

5. It brings psychiatric nurses into a closer working relationship with general nurses to their mutual advantage;

6. It enhances the development of specialist psychiatric out-patient care by linking it to the out-patient facilities which are already available for other specialties at the general hospital;

7. It makes long-term economic sense by enabling the psychiatric in-patient unit to share services and facilities at the general hospital.

7.43   While these benefits are considerable, we recognise that a policy of integrating psychiatry with the general hospital service also gives rise to problems.

1. Some capital investment in the provision of psychiatric units at general hospitals will be required. This problem is acute at a time of recession when there are many demands for the limited investment resources available. However, the amount of capital required for psychiatric development would form but a relatively small part of the total capital investment planned for general hospital services while the benefits, both in treatment and in economic terms, could be considerable. This matter is more fully considered in Chapter 15.

2. There is a danger that a declared policy of transferring in-patient care from psychiatric hospitals to general hospitals will seriously affect the morale of staff working in the psychiatric hospitals. This danger must be anticipated and countered. This can be done by a positive approach on the part of the leaders of the local psychiatric service in planning and providing a comprehensive service. The psychiatric hospitals will have an essential function in this service for many years to come and it should be made quite clear that the phasing-out of these hospitals is a gradual process which is dependent on the build-up of a range of alternative services.

3. The staff of general hospitals may be uneasy at the prospect of taking all psychiatric admissions from a designated catchment area. This will arise from the traditional perception of the type of patient resident in psychiatric hospitals. It must be remembered, however, that this

picture is changing and will be radically altered in the context of a comprehensive psychiatric service. Moreover, old long-stay patients will not be admitted to general hospital psychiatric units and special arrangements in secure units will be made for the small number of patients who may be severely disturbed.

7.44   A general hospital which has a psychiatric unit should be associated with a designated catchment area. It should meet in full the psychiatric in-patient requirements of that area. These arrangements should be associated with the development of community services and the re-organisation of the role of the psychiatric hospital as outlined in this Report. We recommend that the adoption of catchment area responsibility by general hospital psychiatric units should be completed by the end of 1985 at the latest.

Voluntary Hospitals

7.45   We have examined the arrangements, particularly those in the Eastern Health Board area, relating to a psychiatric service being provided by public voluntary hospitals. We consider that the service should be provided on the same basis as that in a health board hospital. This means that the hospital should meet all the psychiatric in-patient requirements of a designated catchment area. It also means that health board consultant psychiatrists should be included in the staff of public voluntary and joint board hospitals which provide a psychiatric service. As new general hospitals come on stream the opportunity should be availed of to appoint health board psychiatrists to the staff of these hospitals. This will help to integrate the psychiatric service and will ensure that hospitals provide the appropriate components of a comprehensive psychiatric service to persons in their catchment area.

Transition Arrangements

7.46   In areas which do not yet have a psychiatric unit associated with a general hospital, such units should now be planned. We consider that the programme of providing psychiatric units in general hospitals should be accelerated because the need for this form of in-patient service is urgent. While this programme is proceeding, sectors which do not yet have access to a general hospital psychiatric service should experiment with various ways of providing an in-patient service. Each sector should try to provide the type of service which best simulates the service provided in a general hospital unit.

Screening Admissions

7.47   The tradition of the local psychiatric hospital, as a place of asylum where a person was looked after and given shelter, continues and many hospitals are slow to turn away people seeking help. In the past, many persons were inappropriately admitted to psychiatric hospitals because they had nowhere else to go. If there is to be a significant reduction in the number of new admissions to psychiatric hospitals, strict admission criteria must be established. These criteria should ensure that persons who are admitted are genuinely in need of in-patient care and that they come from a sector served by the hospital. For example, an assessment unit was set up in St Brendan's Hospital, Dublin to ensure that no patient is admitted to hospital without having been thoroughly assessed. The operation of this unit has caused a marked reduction in the number of admissions to the hospital.[16, 17, 18]

7.48   Admission to hospital should be considered by the sector team only if it is not possible to provide the required treatment on an out-patient or day basis. This requires that the in-patient service should be complementary to a range of services in the community.

7.49   **Recommendations**

1. **Psychiatric in-patient facilities should cater for all psychiatric patients from a designated catchment area who need in-patient care (para. 7.9).**

2. **Psychiatrists in psychiatric units in general hospitals should provide a liaison psychiatry service within the general hospital (para. 7.11).**

3. **The planning guideline for in-patient services for short-stay and medium-stay patients should be 0.5 beds per 1,000 total population (para. 7.16).**

4. **Each psychiatric hospital should estimate the number of beds needed for old long-stay patients to the end of this century. One approach to this question is set out in Appendix 4 (para. 7.20).**

5. **The potential for discharging old long-stay patients to community residential accommodation should be fully explored. All patients should be provided with rehabilitation programmes appropriate to their needs (para. 7.23).**

6. **The in-patient service for new long-stay patients should be located in high support hostels (para. 7.25).**

7. **Mentally ill persons who require in-patient services in conditions of security should be accommodated in secure units provided in regional centres. A separate study should be carried**

out in order to determine the number of places required in these units (para. 7.28).

8. The planning guideline for in-patient services for new long-stay patients aged under 65 should be set at 0.2 beds per 1,000 total population and the planning guideline for new long-stay patients aged over 65 should be set at 2.5 beds per 1,000 population aged 65 or over (equivalent to about 0.3 beds per 1,000 total population) (para. 7.30 and 7.31).

9. Mentally handicapped persons in psychiatric hospitals should be segregated from the mentally ill and provided with programmes of care and activity appropriate to their needs. The mental handicap service should take over responsibility for these persons when this has been achieved (para. 7.37).

10. Disturbed mentally handicapped persons should be catered for within the mental handicap service (para. 7.38).

11. Where there are large numbers of elderly persons in psychiatric hospitals whose needs are primarily geriatric they should be accommodated separately from the mentally ill. The geriatric service should be involved in this process and in organising appropriate programmes of care for these patients (para. 7.40).

12. Ideally, the in-patient service for all admissions should be provided in psychiatric units in general hospitals (para. 7.9 and para.s 7.41 to 7.44).

13. Health board consultant psychiatrists should be included in the staff of all public voluntary and joint board hospitals which provide a psychiatric service (para. 7.45).

14. Strict admission criteria should be introduced in all psychiatric hospitals (para. 7.47 and 7.48).

Chapter 8

Out-Patient Clinics

Definition

8.1   Specialist out-patient clinics are essential to a comprehensive psychiatric service. Their primary objective is to provide assessment, diagnosis and treatment under the supervision of a consultant psychiatrist to mentally ill persons. When located in the community as an integral part of a comprehensive service, the out-patient clinic is well placed to establish links with the patient and his relatives in a familiar social environment. Out-patient clinics provide an important resource for general practitioners by enabling them to treat many conditions which would otherwise require in-patient care. For the patient, out-patient services ensure continued contact with society and professional supervision of his illness without the disruption caused by hospital admission.

Present Operation of Out-Patient Clinics

8.2   In the year ended 31 May, 1983 psychiatric out-patient clinics were held at 211 locations. There were 200,321 out-patient attendances; 7% were new and 93% were repeat attendances. The total number of persons who attended these clinics in this one year period was 45,197, a rate of 13.1 per 1000 population.[1]

8.3   The effectiveness of out-patient clinics as they now operate is open to question. For example, it has been shown from the psychiatric case registers kept for Counties Carlow, Westmeath and Roscommon and the catchment area of St. Loman's Hospital, Dublin that general practitioners do not resume care of patients following specialist out-patient psychiatric treatment.[2,3] Similarly, in a study by Keane and Fahy[4] of the aftercare of over 200 patients discharged from St. Loman's Hospital the authors concluded that the psychiatric service ran the risk of being seriously isolated from the primary care and general medical services. A spot check on the work of the St. Loman's out-patient clinics revealed that 85% of the patients attending were former in-patients. It was found in this study that:

56

"the typical out-patient attender had a long history of out-patient care, numerous previous admissions, and previous experience of hostel or day care. Out-patient attenders tended significantly to be unmarried, unemployed and educationally handicapped, compared with the remainder of the case material".

8.4   Data from both the case registers and the study by Keane and Fahy indicate that out-patient clinics at present provide mainly a follow-up and maintenance service for mentally ill patients. We envisage a more dynamic role for out-patient clinics, incorporating a referral service for general practitioners, an assessment and diagnostic service and a treatment service including psychotherapy and behaviour therapy for all categories of psychiatric patients. We recognise that it may be difficult to develop a broader role for out-patient clinics not least because there is a tendency for clinics to become "blocked up" with chronic patients. One method of overcoming this problem may be for each team to provide separate clinics for long-term patients.

Organisation of Out-Patient Services

8.5   Out-patient clinics should be provided by the sector team in centres in their sector. A consultant psychiatrist should attend at every clinic. Referral to an out-patient clinic will usually be made by a general practitioner requesting the opinion of a consultant psychiatrist on a patient. Requests to out-patient clinics for advice will also be made by social workers, psychologists and by other health workers and helping agencies in the community. A primary concern of the psychiatrist should be to determine the stage at which the patient can be returned to the care of the general practitioner. It will not be possible to refer the patient back in all cases. Some patients will need treatment which can be provided only by specialist psychiatric staff and they will require repeat visits to out-patient clinics. This group includes a number of long-term patients living in unsupervised accommodation in the community. The maintenance in the community of this group of patients, many of whom are schizophrenics, may require home visits by psychiatric nurses in association with regular out-patient attendance. However, it is to be expected that the majority of patients will be referred back to their general practitioner for continuing care and treatment and monitoring of progress.

8.6   A high proportion, perhaps the majority, of patients attending an out-patient clinic will be repeat attenders. Nevertheless, if general practitioners seek consultant opinion on the psychiatric problems of their patients and consultants refer the patients back to the general practitioners for continuing treatment, then new patients should form a large part of the consultant out-patient workload. In Chapter 5 we have made a case for strengthening the links between general practitioners and consultant psychiatrists. One way of measuring the success which is being achieved in doing this is by the extent to which out-patient clinics are used for the assessment of new patients.

Dispensing of Drugs

8.7   The practice of dispensing drugs without charge at out-patient clinics has encouraged many people to attend these clinics to ensure a regular and cost-free supply of drugs. In most health board areas this practice has been discontinued and this has been followed by a favourable change in the ratio of new to old patients. Since patients were referred back to their general practitioners for prescriptions, an added bonus was better communication between the specialist psychiatric service and the general practitioner. The total number of out-patient attendances also fell considerably and this meant that the consultant had more time to spend with each patient and to develop a proper consultation service.

8.8   We are not concerned here with the matter of supplying drugs without charge but we do consider that this practice should be examined to determine whether the objective is to make available psychiatric drugs without charge and if so, whether this objective could be met in a way which does not encourage patients to attend clinics unnecessarily.

Importance of an Appointment System and Pleasant Surroundings

8.9   The absence of an appointment system in many clinics creates difficulties for patients and doctors and detracts from the quality of the service. We recommend that there should be a Secretary/Receptionist attached to clinics who would organise an efficient appointment system. We also recommend that the premises where out-patient clinics are held should be maintained to a high standard. The accommodation should be made as cheerful and comfortable as possible for the people attending there.

Location and Frequency of Clinics

8.10   We recommend that the sector team hold out-patient clinics in the principal towns in the sector. If a general hospital has a psychiatric unit, psychiatric clinics should be held in the out-patient department of that hospital. There should be at least one clinic in every sector. Where the population being served is reasonably concentrated, it should be possible to confine the venues for out-patient clinics to a small number of centres. This has the obvious advantage of reducing the amount of time the team has to spend on the road. Where the population is more scattered, it will be necessary to hold clinics in a larger number of locations so that patients do not have to travel long distances to attend. The frequency of clinics should vary with the level of demand. In general, we recommend frequent clinics in a central location rather than less frequent clinics in outlying venues.

8.11 Recommendations

1. Each sector psychiatric team should hold out-patient clinics incorporating an assessment and diagnostic service and a treatment service (para. 8.4).

2. A prime function of out-patient clinics should be to provide a consultation service to general practitioners and other community health personnel (para. 8.4 and 8.5).

3. Treatment of a kind not normally provided by general practitioners will need to be provided on a continuing basis at out-patient clinics for some long-term patients living in the community (para. 8.5).

4. The practice of dispensing drugs without charge at out-patient clinics should be reviewed (para. 8.8).

5. There should be a Secretary/Receptionist attached to clinics who would be responsible for organising an efficient appointment system (para. 8.9).

6. The premises where out-patient clinics are held should be well maintained and decorated (para. 8.9).

7. Out-patient clinics should be held in the principal towns in each sector (para. 8.10).

8. Where practicable there should be frequent clinics in a central location rather than less frequent clinics in outlying venues (para. 8.10).

Chapter 9

Community-Based Residences

Introduction

9.1 Community orientation in the psychiatric service recognises that the people for whom the services are provided live in the community. In general, this presents no problem but residential facilities are required for those persons who for various reasons cannot live in their own homes. Broadly, these persons are:

—persons now living in psychiatric hospitals who have no homes of their own to return to but who, with adequate preparation and training, would be capable of living a reasonable life in the community;

—persons coming forward for psychiatric care with chronic psychiatric disability, who have inadequate or no homes and who would be capable of living with varying degrees of independence in accommodation in the community;

—persons with psychiatric problems whose treatment requires that they live apart from their family or normal associates for a while — such persons include disturbed teenagers who have family difficulties and patients in need of temporary accommodation due to any of a variety of social reasons;

—the small group of new long-stay patients for whom high support hostels will provide an alternative to long-stay hospital care. The accommodation needs of this group were described in paragraphs 7.24 and 7.25.

We firmly believe that many persons from these four categories could be suitably placed in community residences if the preparatory measures which are described in this chapter are implemented. This conviction is based not only on theory but has been demonstrated in practice.

Types of Residence

9.2 The term "hostel" is generally used to describe a residence which accommodates a number of patients in the community. There is, however, a wider range of options which may be considered and this term does not adequately cover them all. The types of residence considered in this chapter are:

—Domestic scale residences

—Flats

—Lodgings

—Supervised hostels

—High support hostels

—Accommodation attached to day facilities.

Present Provision of Hostels

9.3 Some residential facilities have now been developed by all health boards. In 1981 there were 95 hostels for the mentally ill in the country. The general trend is for an increase in the number of hostels in all health board areas. The number of existing hostel places and the rate per 100,000 population are shown in Table 9.1. It may be seen from this table that there is considerable variation between health boards in the extent to which hostels have been provided.

TABLE 9.1

Number of hostel places in December 1983 and rate per 100,000 population in each health board area (1981 Census of Population)

Health Board Area	Number of hostels	Number of hostel places	Number of hostel places per 100,000 population
Eastern	32	352	29.5
Midland	7	35	17.3
Mid-Western	8	99	32.1
North-Eastern	20	129	44.6
North-Western	10	66	31.7
South-Eastern	16	96	25.6
Southern	6	76	14.4
Western	12	89	26.1
TOTAL	111	942	27.3

Source: Department of Health.

Domestic Scale Residences

9.4 Many persons with psychiatric disability live normally in their own homes or with relatives or friends, using the various community psychiatric

61

and other support facilities which are available to them. They derive considerable benefit from taking responsibility for the activities of everyday life. There are other people, many of whom live in psychiatric hospitals, who could enjoy a normal existence in the community but because they do not have, or are unable to set up, a suitable home, are denied the benefits of such a way of life. It is quite feasible to offer them the alternative of living in a domestic residence, which would improve the quality of their lives and which would not in any way interfere with the way of life of their neighbours.

9.5   An extensive rehousing programme of hospitalised patients has been successfully implemented in the Cavan/Monaghan area.[1] Several houses have been rented in the area mainly from the local housing authority. These houses are located in housing estates in both urban and rural settings and the majority have three bedrooms and are semi-detached. Three or four persons live in each house. The residents cater for their own needs — shopping, preparing meals, cleaning and maintaining the house. They work or attend day centres during the day and take part in the recreational activities of their neighbourhood. All expenses involved in running the house, including rent, are paid from the residents' own income. Income may come from wages or from the Disabled Persons Maintenance Allowance. In the period 1975 to 1981 some 140 persons were discharged from St. Davnet's Hospital to these houses. Fifty of them were able to return to live with their relatives after spending some time in the houses. Twenty returned to the hospital. The remaining seventy were still living in the houses at the end of 1981.

9.6   A key factor in the rehousing programme was the careful selection of suitable persons and detailed training and preparation before the transfer was made. A social rehabilitation unit has been set up in the hospital to train patients in the skills of everyday living. They learn how to manage a house and how to relate to people in the course of normal living. There are two houses in the grounds of the hospital where patients live for a time, simulating normal living conditions, before they move to an estate house. it is only after a vigorous training programme, which normally lasts several months and in many cases well over a year, that a patient is accepted for transfer.

Acquisition of Houses

9.7   We envisage that there would be three main sources of accommodation for a rehousing programme viz.

—health board

—local housing authority

—voluntary organisations

62

It is important to the success of such a programme that the health board establish a good relationship with the local housing authority. In some parts of the country the local authority allocates one house in all new schemes for mentally ill persons. A member of the sector team should be assigned responsibility for liaising with the housing authorities to obtain their assistance in the acquisition of houses. This person should also liaise with voluntary organisations such as the Mental Health Association which may wish to become involved in obtaining houses for patients. Houses provided by voluntary organisations may be more acceptable to the local community than those provided by public bodies.

Guidelines

9.8   We consider that a rehousing programme for psychiatric patients should be strengthened and vigorously pursued in every health board area. The following guidelines are offered to help achieve this objective:

1. A thorough assessment of all psychiatric patients resident in the psychiatric hospital should be carried out to ascertain the nature and level of handicap and the potential of housing to meet their needs.

2. There should be a formal process of preparing patients for transfer to a residential setting in each hospital. This matter is dealt with in greater detail in paragraphs 9.19 to 9.21 below. Care should be taken to ensure that the persons chosen to live together are compatible. One person in each house could be invited to act as leader of the group living in that house.

3. Normal domestic residences in residential areas should be acquired. Preference should be given by the health boards to renting houses. The local housing authority and voluntary groups should be involved in the provision of suitable houses.

4. One or more members of the sector psychiatric team should be given responsibility for supervising the houses and their residents. This is important for the successful follow-up of patients and in particular to ensure immediate help should any problems arise.

5. Arrangements should be made to ensure ready access by the residents to whatever psychiatric services they require. These include day care and rehabilitation and to a lesser extent, out-patient clinics. Patients who suffer a relapse may need to be admitted for a period of in-patient treatment. The member of the sector team with responsibility for such patients should follow their progress and ensure that when discharged they are able to return to the same house.

6. Responsibility for negotiating with the housing authority should be

63

assigned to a designated person who should also give assistance to voluntary organisations who co-operate in the rehousing programme.

Independent Flats

9.9   Another form of accommodation in the community without resident staff is the independent flat. Flat schemes have been introduced in Finland and the United Kingdom for rehousing psychiatric patients. The evidence suggests that they cater for a population very similar to those in houses in the community.[2] An effort should be made to acquire a number of flats in the same building so that the rehoused patients will have some measure of group support but yet maintain some privacy and independence. There is a danger with such schemes that the patient becomes isolated and cut-off from social contact. In Finland a number of flats are provided in the same building.[3] One flat is occupied by a person who acts as "warden" and who deals with any problems the patients may encounter. We consider that a less formal arrangement would also be feasible, for example the landlord or a tenant who is not a former patient could act as warden with support from a psychiatric nurse. The psychiatric nurse would visit the patients regularly and would be "on-call" to the warden should any problems arise.

Lodgings

9.10   In some areas psychiatric patients have been placed in lodgings. These arrangements may vary considerably. Sometimes a number of patients are placed in the same household. Alternatively, patients may be in "digs" with a resident landlady or landlord. While experience of lodgings to date in this country has been limited, a strong case can be made in favour of a lodging or boarding-out arrangement.[4] The patient benefits through everyday contact with other people. Householders who care for the welfare of their lodgers can help them to maintain a stable way of life. An expansion of these arrangements would move resources spent in caring for patients from institutions to the community. At a time of receding employment, it could be a most welcome opportunity for many householders to increase their income by offering a caring service.

9.11   A lodging arrangement for a psychiatric patient needs to be carefully planned and controlled. The patients selected must be thoroughly prepared before they move into lodgings. They need a planned programme of activities during the day. Regular contact should be maintained with the patients in the boarding house so that its suitability can be reviewed and approval withdrawn if circumstances justify it. Responsibility for acquiring and supervising lodgings should be given to a designated member of the sector team with a nursing qualification. He or she should be responsible for ensuring that patients are being properly looked after in their lodgings and monitoring their condition. It is important that there should be good communication between householders who provide lodgings and the sector team so that any problems arising with the patients can be resolved quickly. The assurance that help is readily available in times of crisis will undoubtedly influence householders in deciding to take lodgers. The patients concerned should be able to pay the boarding charges from their own income, for example, the Disabled Persons Maintenance Allowance or Old Age Pension. If necessary, financial assistance towards meeting these payments might be provided by the health board.

9.12 One of the most important factors in the success of lodgings is the personality and motivation of the householder.[5] This person should not be motivated by purely financial considerations but should be genuinely interested in the patients. Someone active in community activities in the area might be suitable for this job. The suitability of the premises should be judged by reference to the

—accessibility of its location,

—acceptability of room size for the patient/s,

—comfort of furnishings and household conveniences,

—and whether or not it has a telephone.

A preparatory course should be arranged for persons intending to receive patients as lodgers. Instruction should be given on the nature of mental illness, how it affects behaviour and the type of problems which may arise with patients. This induction course should be supplemented by regular refresher courses for householders.

9.13 We consider that there is potential for placing many more psychiatric patients in lodgings. We recommend that every health board should set up a lodging scheme on a pilot basis and that policy and practice on lodging patients should be refined in the light of the results of these pilot schemes.

Supervised Hostel

9.14 The special feature of a supervised hostel is the presence of a resident supervisor. Such a hostel provides a home for persons with long-term mental illness who could not manage without supervision. The supervisor acts as a general administrator and lends support and reassurance to the residents. He or she need not necessarily have a nursing or other professional qualification. It is to be expected that many patients will move on from the supervised hostel to a more independent way of life such as a domestic residence, lodgings or a flat. Care should be taken in the selection of a person for the post of supervisor. The supervised hostel should be small in size to avoid an institutional atmosphere. We consider that it should normally have an upper limit of eight to ten residents. Where possible, it should be located in a residential area. It may need to be purpose-built or possibly two adjoining houses in a housing estate could be redesigned as one living unit with one shared kitchen and living room.

9.15   We do not yet have experience in this country of hostels which cater for different categories of patients, for example psychiatric and geriatric patients. We feel that a mixed, supervised hostel might be successful, particularly in an area which would not justify a hostel catering for only one category of patients.

9.16   The supervised hostel could help treat patients. It might be used to accommodate persons, such as young schizophrenics, who need to live away from their family environment.

High Support Hostel

9.17   In paragraph 7.25 we recommended that high support hostels, with 24-hour nursing care, should provide accommodation for the small group of new long-stay patients. In view of the treatment function of these hostels, they should be larger than normal supervised hostels and we have recommended that they should cater for 15-20 patients. These hostels provide long-stay care in the community as an alternative to long-stay care in psychiatric hospitals. They can be linked to local day care facilities and allow people to be cared for closer to their relatives. The development of high support hostels is an important step in the transition to a time when the large psychiatric hospitals will no longer be needed and we consider that they should be regarded as a priority for development.

Accommodation attached to day facilities

9.18   Some mental health centres might have a number of supervised hostel places at their disposal. These beds could be used for assessment, treatment and crisis intervention, particularly for patients who live some distance from the mental health centre.

Preparation for Transfer to Community Residences

9.19   The rehousing of psychiatric patients will not be successful unless it is accompanied by a programme to prepare patients for coping with the demands of everyday living. The first requirement is that hospital patients should be thoroughly and expertly assessed to determine their level of handicap and their potential for rehabilitation and for independent community living. The second and main requirement is a formally organised system of training patients in social skills. The programme should normally include:

— training in social skills to help patients surmount the problems of everyday life, improve their self-reliance, their capacity to deal with emergencies and to manage their medication;

— experience of the activities of daily living such as shopping, cooking, cleaning, budgeting and looking after money, as well as training in habits of good personal hygiene;

— instruction in reading, writing and self-expression;

— training in occupational skills to teach work practices and establish the work habit.

9.20 Persons who have lived in a hospital for some years cannot readily adapt to life outside the hospital. Many of them may need to be carefully and painstakingly tutored in basic procedures and skills which most people take for granted. A multidisciplinary input to rehabilitation is necessary with contributions from special therapists such as domestic economy instructors, beauticians, recreational therapists, in addition to the usual team members. The question of rehabilitation is dealt with in Chapter 10.

Training Hostel

9.21 A house which simulates the conditions of a domestic residence in the community and which may be used for preparing patients for discharge is an important part of any training programme. Such houses, or training hostels, have been set up in a number of areas and have proved very successful. We recommend that this useful development should be adopted generally in the psychiatric hospitals as part of an active programme of discharging suitably trained patients from the existing long-stay population into an appropriate community residential setting. Training hostels have tended to be set up in the grounds of psychiatric hospital but they might also be located at some distance from the hospital. The choice of location for a training hostel will depend on local circumstances.

Setting up Residential Facilities

9.22 To ensure a favourable public reaction to the placing of psychiatric patients in community residences, the initial move needs to be very carefully planned. The most important factor is to prepare the patients properly so that they will be able to cope with their new life. In a number of countries the failure to prepare patients adequately before discharging them to accommodation in the community led to general disillusionment and criticism of the concept of community care by members of the general public. If neighbours are helpful and friendly to the patients in a community residence, it will ease many potential difficulties. It is also important to select the patients carefully so that they will be able to live together compatibly. There should be at least one patient in each residential unit who could be relied on to act responsibly should a crisis arise. As patients are moved out to accommodation in the community, the beds previously occupied by these patients in the psychiatric hospital should be removed.

Activities for Residents in Accommodation in the Community

9.23   The primary objective of residential accommodation in the community is to provide a comfortable and secure home for the people living there. However, the residents in community accommodation are at risk of social withdrawal and of under-activity unless they have something to do during the daytime.[6] It is not sufficient to make available a living environment and leave the rest to work itself out.

9.24   Ideally, community accommodation should provide a homely environment for a person who goes out to work during normal working hours and takes part in the various social and recreational activities of the area. However, many residents in community accommodation will not be capable of this level of occupation and they may become isolated. The community residential facility should be fully integrated with the other components of the psychiatric service located in the area, such as day facilities and sheltered workshops. The sector team, and particularly the psychiatric nurse, should ensure that all the residents in community accommodation are occupied during the day. The nurse might get in touch with local employers to secure employment for patients residing in community accommodation in the area. The residents in community accommodation will also have access to the placement service operated by the National Rehabilitation Board. In the case of patients who are not successful in obtaining or maintaining open or sheltered employment, arrangements should be made for them to attend the local day facility.

Number of Places in Community Residential Accommodation

9.25   In coming to a conclusion on the number of places required in community residential accommodation it is helpful to review the evidence which is now available on this matter.

1. The Department of Health and Social Security (London) Report "Better Services for the Mentally Ill"[7] put forward a guideline of 20 to 30 residential places per 100,000 population with places in homes

supervised by staff accounting for about one third of the total. Experience to date in this country suggests that a much greater provision is required.

2. Experience during the past twelve years in St Davnet's Hospital, Monaghan suggests an initial maximum requirement of 100 places for a population of 100,000 falling to about 80 places as the backlog of existing long-stay patients is reduced.

3. The experience in the St. Loman's Hospital, Dublin catchment area is that 30-40 places in unsupervised accommodation and about 20 places in supervised hostels are needed for a catchment area of 260,000 population (or 20-23 places per 100,000 population). There is no backlog of "old" long-stay patients in St. Loman's but there is a small number of patients in these hostels who need to be re-admitted to the hospital from time to time.

4. In the planning project which has been carried out in St. Ita's Hospital, Portrane the project team has estimated that if a programme to provide community residences for both existing long-stay and new long-stay patients is implemented, a total of about 100 residential places, or 45 places per 100,000 population will be required. This estimate makes allowances for the care of elderly persons being undertaken by the geriatric services, persons returning to their own homes after spending some time in a hostel and persons needing to be re-admitted to hospital. This estimate would have to be more than doubled if persons aged over 65 were included.

9.26   On the basis of the experience in these and other hospitals, we estimate that the requirement for community residential accommodation in a catchment area of 100,000 population with a backlog of existing long-stay patients would initially approach 100 places with one quarter to one third of these places in supervised hostels. The long-term requirement would be considerably lower than this and would probably be in the region of 60 places per 100,000 population. This is the requirement we would estimate for a catchment area of 100,000 population without a backlog of existing long-stay patients. High support hostel places, referred to in paragraphs 7.24 and 7.25 and again in paragraph 9.17, are not included in this provision.

9.27   **Recommendations**

1. **Each sector team should provide a range of residential accommodation in the community as outlined in para.s 9.4 to 9.18, to to house former hospital patients and to cater for the needs of**

mentally ill persons living in unsatisfactory accommodation in the community.

2. A programme to rehouse hospitalised, mentally ill patients should be implemented by every health board. Training hostels should be established in all hospitals as part of this programme (para. 9.8 and 9.19 to 9.21).

3. The sector team should ensure that all the residents in community accommodation are occupied during the day. Some residents may obtain work in open or sheltered employment while others will attend daily at the day facility (para. 9.23 and 9.24).

4. We set a planning guideline of about 100 places (with one quarter to one third of these places in supervised hostels) in community residential accommodation for a catchment area of 100,000 population with a backlog of existing long-stay patients. We set a planning guideline of 60 places in community residential accommodation for a catchment area of 100,000 population without a backlog of existing long-stay patients (para. 9.26).

Chapter 10

Rehabilitation

10.1 Rehabilitation in psychiatry is concerned with returning skills to a person who has had them impaired by mental illness. It also involves training in new skills. These skills foster the ability of individuals to cope in domestic, occupational, industrial, social and recreational settings.

10.2 The steady decline over the last two decades in the number of patients resident in psychiatric hospitals has been one of the most encouraging developments in the psychiatric service. The potential for continuing this trend cannot be fully realised without formal programmes of rehabilitation. Such programmes, aimed at re-integrating psychiatric patients into the community, must be a central and inegrral part of care and treatment services.

Report of the Working Party on Occupational Therapy/Industrial Therapy Services within the Psychiatric Service

10.3 The Working Party on Occupational Therapy/Industrial Therapy Services[1] reported in November 1981, setting out detailed guidelines for the future development of rehabilitation within the psychiatric service. The report stressed the need for the provision of comprehensive rehabilitation programmes for all patients in psychiatric hospitals and outlined the important role of the psychiatric nurse in implementing such programmes. We consider that this report provides an indispensable guide to health boards in planning and organising rehabilitation services for the mentally ill in hospital and community settings.

Present State

10.4 The rate at which rehabilitation services have developed up to now has been haphazard, uneven and less than satisfactory. There is considerable scope for improvement.

10.5 Figures collected by the Department of Health in 1981 indicated that hospital based industrial/occupational therapy units were catering, either full-time or part-time, for 2,600 in-patients or 21 per cent of the public psychiatric in-patient population. A service was also provided for about 300 day patients. In addition, two independent units outside the psychiatric service were providing industrial therapy for about 100 psychiatric in-patients.

Programme of Rehabilitation

10.6   It is a fundamental principle of modern psychiatric rehabilitation that each patient is assessed individually and, following assessment, receives therapy which is specifically designed to alleviate his or her disabilities. Assessment aims at identifying the patient's psychiatric disabilities, together with his or her personal strengths. The main elements of such an assessment are described in the Working Party's report referred to in paragraph 10.3.[1] Following assessment, a specially designed programme of rehabilitation should be drawn up for each patient aimed at cultivating social, communication and vocational skills. This programme should be clearly planned and should set out specific goals and methods by which they are to be achieved. There should be regular review of goals and methods of attainment so that the effectiveness of the rehabilitation programme can be assessed.

Social Training

10.7   With the reduction in the number of in-patients in psychiatric hospitals in recent years the remaining long-stay patients include a greater proportion of persons who are elderly or who have serious social handicaps. The traditional emphasis on industrial and work skills in rebabilitation programmes has not the same relevance for these patients. They need a programme of rehabilitation which emphasises social and communication skills. This type of training is essential if they are to succeed in living outside the hospital setting.

Special Rehabilitation Ward

10.8   The Working Party[1] recommended a special rehabilitation ward in every psychiatric hospital as an important initial step towards the provision of a comprehensive rehabilitation programme. We consider that this recom-mendation should be fully implemented. While the main function of this ward relates to the teaching of social and daily living skills to patients, it will also have an equally important role as a resource centre for all other wards of the hospital. Nurses can improve their therapeutic skills in this ward to rehabilitate more patients in other wards in the hospital.

72

Rehabilitation in Long-Stay Wards

10.9 While specialised skills and techniques can best be developed in a special rehabilitation ward, active rehabilitation should be a normal feature of every long-stay ward. Long-stay wards which do not have active rehabilitation programmes (and there are still many of these) tend to have a negative atmosphere with the role of the nurses largely limited to custodial care. Modern rehabilitation programmes, when properly planned and implemented, can improve this situation by creating an air of activity and optimism. In hospitals where rehabilitation programmes for long-stay patients are the norm, they have had very positive effects, not only in realising the potential of patients, but also in improving the moral and job satisfaction of nursing, medical and other staff.

Patients with Little Prospect of Discharge

10.10 It is likely that some patients in the psychiatric hospitals will be unable to return to the community. This may be as a result of their advanced years, the particular nature or severity of their psychiatric disability or the cumulative effect of many years of inactive institutional living. For these patients, exposure to a broad range of rehabilitation activities and social programmes plays an essential part in improving the quality of their lives.

Need for Leadership

10.11 Active programmes of rehabilitation do not occur automatically. They require considerable foresight, drive and commitment by the senior members of hospital management — medical, nursing and administrative. If leadership at senior management level is absent, it is naive to expect that the required programmes of rehabilitation will be initiated.

Drawing up a Programme of Rehabilitation

10.12 Responsibility for the provision of psychiatric rehabilitation services lies with the Programme Manager for Special Hospitals of each health board and with the senior administrative, medical and nursing personnel in each hospital. Individual hospital staff should be assigned specific responsibility for the development and implementation of comprehensive rehabilitation programmes for all patients. We agree with the recommendation of the Working Party[1] that a team composed of a consultant psychiatrist, an assistant chief nursing officer and a senior administrator should as a first step draw up an outline plan for the provision of rehabilitation programmes for approval by the Programme Manager. Review and modification should be built into each scheme so that programmes can be regularly up-dated.

The Role of the Psychiatric Nurse

10.13   While modern rehabilitation programmes require a multidisciplinary approach, the psychiatric nurse has a central role because of the close and constant relationship which he or she enjoys with the patient. The aim of psychiatric nursing is to restore the patient to health and to achieve the maximum improvement of his or her disability as a prelude to discharge from hospital. Where discharge from hospital is not feasible, nurses are responsible for improving the quality of life for long-stay patients. It follows that activation and therapy are central to successful nursing and that nurses should be actively involved in planning, implementing and monitoring various rehabilitation programmes at ward level with other members of the hospital staff.

10.14   To realise the potential of nurses to rehabilitate patients, it is essential that the traditional custodial role of nursing change finally to one of therapy and of improving the capabilities of the patient. This change in the nursing role is happening with every encouraging results but it needs to be accelerated and applied in all hospitals. An appreciation of what can be achieved in the development of rehabilitation programmes, once a commitment is made and leadership of the right calibre is given, has been lacking.

10.15   The current training syllabus for psychiatric nurses needs to be revised to bring it up to date with the changing role of nursing. In particular, those elements which deal with rehabilitation and therapeutic techniques need to be expanded and developed. This is not to suggest that nurses now working in the psychiatric services are unsuited to participating in rehabilitation programmes nor does it justify in any way a reluctance by some nurses to become involved in this essential work.

10.16   In addition to the psychiatric nurse, other professional groups also have an important role in comprehensive rehabilitation programmes. These include occupational therapists, physical education instructors, speech therapists, literacy teachers and others who can use their own specialist expertise to enhance hospital therapy programmes.

Rehabilitation Services within the Community

10.17   The primary aim of rehabilitation programmes is to re-integrate mentally ill persons with their community. It follows that rehabilitation services within hospitals should have a strong community orientation and

74

must, if they are to be effective, be accompanied by a simultaneous development of support facilities in the community. The various types of day care facilities and living accommodation described in Chapters 6 and 9 of this report form an important part of the network of rehabilitation services needed in the community.

10.18   Many persons living at home or in community residential accommodation need rehabilitation services. The patient should be thoroughly assessed and offered rehabilitation geared to meet his or her needs. A rehabilitation service should always be provided on a day attendance basis and would in many cases form a large part of the service provided at day facilities. In addition to social care, day centres should provide a wide range of industrial therapy and occupational activities.

Vocational Rehabilitation

10.19   Mental illness often adversely affects an individual's ability to occupy him or herself constructively or to pursue normal employment. The many different types of mental illness and the varying degrees of recovery among patients, produce a corresponding diversity in the needs of the mentally ill for vocational rehabilitation. These needs can be met by training in new skills, sheltered employment and open employment.

Training in New Skills and Sheltered Employment

10.20   Training in new skills and sheltered employment are provided in industrial therapy units attached to psychiatric hospitals and in community workshops. Industrial therapy units attached to psychiatric hospitals cater primarily for psychiatric in-patients but figures collected by the Department of Health for 1983 show that some 500 patients living in the community also attend these units[2]. Various work activities are provided ranging from unskilled work, such as assembly and packaging on a contract basis, to more skilled work such as woodwork, metalwork, maintenance work. It is likely that for the majority of persons attending who live in the community the industrial therapy units provide long-term sheltered employment.

10.21   The Working Party on Training and Employing the Handicapped,[3] which reported in 1975, recommended that community workshops be developed firstly, for the activation and training of handicapped persons, and secondly, for the provision of sheltered employment for those who have difficulty in obtaining or retaining open employment. Community workshops were to be open to all who might benefit from them, irrespective of their form of handicap. Community workshops have been developed on an extensive scale, mainly on the initiative of the Rehabilitation Institute and the health boards. Funding from the European Social Fund has financed many of these workshops. At the end of 1983 there were about 1000 psychiatric patients attending community/sheltered workshops daily.[2] Most of the community workshops cater for persons who are mentally ill, physically disabled or mentally handicapped. There are also some workshops which cater for mentally ill persons only. These are operated by the health boards or by companies, such as Tolco and Retos Ltd, set up under the aegis of the health boards.

10.22 We agree with paragraph 5.42 of the Green Paper on Services for Disabled People[4] that there is a need for a better balance between workshops for those whose prospects of outside work are reasonably good and for those for whom employment under special conditions for a prolonged period is more likely. We note that the National Rehabilitation Board is to undertake a critical review of the operation of training centres and community workshops to identify any desirable changes. It will also look at the overall need for training and long-term sheltered places and will critically examine the geographic distribution of centres and workshops. We recommend that the needs of mentally ill persons should be taken fully into account in carrying out this review.

10.23 Community workshops would usually cater for mentally ill persons from a number of psychiatric sectors. As in the case of day facilities, it is important to ensure that they are easy to reach by public transport. In city areas workshops should be located on a direct bus or train route.

Co-ordination of Services

10.24 In planning a programme of rehabilitation for patients, it is necessary to distinguish between those capable of benefiting from a community or sheltered workship and those for whom a day centre would be more appropriate. There should be close collaboration during patient assessment between members of the sector team and staff in workshops so that patients are placed in the facility most appropriate to their needs. Similarly, there should be co-ordination between the psychiatric service and the voluntary agencies, such as the Rehabilitation Institute, so that a patient can move easily and quickly from one type of service to another. The population of each sector should have access to a chain of services starting with a day centre providing occupational therapy and other activities and progressing to a community workshop with the possibility of open employment.

10.25 We agree with the recommendation in the Green Paper on Services for Disabled People[4] that health boards should, with the assistance of the National Rehabilitation Board, assess the need for services for disabled persons and plan the development of services, including the establishment of priorities.

76

The need for more vocational rehabilitation services for mentally ill persons should be fully examined as part of this planning exercise.

Open Employment

10.26 Psychiatric patients, in common with all other disabled persons, have access as required to the work placement service operated by the National Rehabilitation Board. In some parts of the country regular meetings are held between the members of the psychiatric team and the National Rehabilitation Board. In addition, we have suggested in Chapter 9 that the psychiatric nurse of the sector team might keep in touch with local employers to try to secure employment for persons living in community-based residences in the area. We consider that mentally ill persons need to be given special support and help in trying to secure employment in the open market. This assistance is particularly necessary now in view of the high level of unemployment generally. We endorse the recommendations made in the Green Paper on Services for Disabled People[4] in regard to furthering employment opportunities for disabled people. We also suggest that the sector team should maintain contact with persons placed in open employment.

10.27 **Recommendations**

1. **Each patient should receive treatment and therapy specifically designed to alleviate his or her individual disabilities, subject to review and appropriate modification on a regular basis (para. 10.6).**

2. **A detailed assessment of each patient should be carried out and, following this, an appropriate programme of rehabilitation should be drawn up (para. 10.6).**

3. **Each hospital should set up a special rehabilitation ward (para. 10.8).**

4. **Active rehabilitation should be a normal and constant feature in every long-stay ward. Patients with little prospect of discharge should also be provided with rehabilitation programmes appropriate to their needs (para. 10.9 and 10.10).**

5. **Individual members of the hospital staff should be assigned specific responsibility for the development and implementation of comprehensive rehabilitation programmes for all patients (para. 10.12).**

6. **Psychiatric nurses should be actively involved in planning, implementing and monitoring various therapy programmes at**

ward level along with other members of the psychiatric hospital staff (para. 10.13 and 10.16).

7. The current training syllabus for psychiatric nurses should be revised and training in rehabilitation and therapeutic techniques should be expanded and developed (para. 10.15).

8. The needs of mentally ill persons should be taken fully into account in the review by the National Rehabilitation Board of training centres and workshops (para. 10.22).

9. The population of each sector should have access to a chain of services starting with a day centre providing occupational therapy and other activities and progressing from there to a community workshop with the possibility of open employment (para. 10.24).

10. In assessing the need for services for disabled persons, health boards should examine the need for more vocational rehabilitation services for mentally ill persons (para. 10.25).

11. Mentally ill persons should be given special support and help by placement officers of the National Rehabilitation Board and by psychiatric nurses in trying to secure employment in the open market (para. 10.26).

Chapter 11

Services for the Elderly Mentally Infirm

Demography

11.1   In 1971 the number of persons aged 65 or over in the State was 330,000. By 1981 this had increased to 369,000 and it has been estimated that by 1991 it will be more than 381,000.[1] The number of persons aged 75 years or over increased from 119,000 to 132,000 between 1971 and 1981. In future years many old people will live alone and social isolation combined with increasing numbers will place a heavy load on the health and social services. In considering the needs of the elderly, it is important to distinguish between the "younger elderly" (65-74 years) group and the "older elderly" (75 years and over) group because disability increases sharply from the mid '70's onwards. Persons aged over 75 years need additional care principally because of an increased incidence of mental illness and intellectual failure. High chronic disability in an increasing number of very elderly persons will place severe pressure on health resources in the years ahead.

Epidemiology

11.2   Elderly persons are at risk from a number of physical and mental illnesses and accurate diagnosis of an elderly person's problem is often complicated because of multiple pathology. Many of these disabilities tend to be of a chronic nature. In considering the psychiatric care of the elderly mentally infirm, it is important to avoid the fallacy that all disturbed elderly persons suffer from dementia. The majority of elderly persons with problems of mental infirmity suffer from functional psychiatric disorders such as depression, paranoid states and neuroses. In many cases these illnesses are linked to physical and social difficulties. Much mental disability in the elderly can be successfully treated. For example, depression is very prevalent among elderly persons but it frequently presents in a masked way and is often mistakenly regarded as dementia by a patient's family and sometimes by the doctor. Considerable benefits can be achieved for the elderly person by treating depressive illness.[2]

11.3   In addition to physical and mental problems, elderly persons tend to suffer from social handicaps. Many live alone and are seldom visited by relatives or friends. In the 1979 Census of Population, 17% of persons aged 65 or over were recorded as living alone and the proportion was as high as 19% in the Eastern Health Board area. This social isolation can have a serious effect on the health of the elderly. Another factor which tends to make the elderly vulnerable as a group is that they constitute a large proportion of the poor and poverty tends to increase with age.

11.4   The conclusion to be drawn from these considerations is that the needs of elderly mentally infirm persons cannot be catered for adequately by the psychiatric service in isolation. The psychiatric service has a role to play but in association with other health and social services. In particular, there should be effective liaison between the psychiatric service and the geriatric and community services.

Prevalence

11.5   The prevalence of mental infirmity in the elderly in this country is not known. Community surveys in the U.K. and elsewhere suggest that between 20% and 25% of the population aged over 65 years suffer from identifiable psychiatric disability.[3, 4, 5] The work of Kay et al.[6] in the 1960's and more recent studies from Northern Europe[5] suggest that the prevalence of severe dementia is of the order of 4% to 5% of the population aged 65 or over. Kay has also found that the prevalence of dementia rises with age; 13% of persons aged over 75 are affected and 20% of those aged over 80. The most recent and satisfactory work on the extent of dementia in the elderly has been carried out in London and New York.[7] The results of this work suggest that in London about 5% of the population aged 65 or over had dementia, compared to 7.5% in New York.

11.6   The Irish Psychiatric Hospital Census, 1981, shows that there were 4,601 patients (excluding mentally handicapped persons) aged 65 or over resident in mental hospitals and units in 1981.[8] This represents 1.2% of the elderly population of this State. An analysis of these patients by broad diagnostic group is given in Table 11.1.

TABLE 11.1

Number of Elderly Patients in Mental Hospitals and Units in 1981 — by age and condition

Age	Organic Psychosis	Functional Illness	Total
65-74	346	2,276	2,622
75 or over	668	1,311	1,979
Total	1,014	3,587	4,601

11.7   A prevalence study by Binchy and Walsh in 1973,[9] of morbidity among persons aged over 70 years receiving care and who were normally living in the catchment area of St. Loman's Psychiatric Hospital, Dublin, showed that for every person with a psychiatric disability being treated by the psychiatric service (in-patient and out-patient) there were two such persons being treated by the geriatric service. If the ratio of this study were to apply to the entire population over 65 the proportion of the elderly population who are both mentally infirm and in institutional care would be about 4%.

11.8   Assuming that, in line with evidence from elsewhere, about 20% to 25% of persons aged 65 or over suffer from some form of mental disability and that less than 5% of the elderly population are both mentally infirm and resident in institutions, it follows that the great majority of elderly mentally infirm persons are living in the community. This highlights the importance of the role of both the primary health care services and the community components of the specialised psychiatric service in the care and management of mental infirmity among the elderly.

Categorising the Elderly Mentally Infirm

11.9   At present mentally infirm elderly persons are cared for by both the psychiatric service and the geriatric service. An important factor which will influence the level of psychiatric support for the elderly is the division of responsibility between these two services. The question arises as to the circumstances in which a patient might be regarded as suffering from an illness which is primarily psychiatric, primarily geriatric, or both psychiatric and geriatric in nature.

11.10   In examining this question, we have categorised elderly mentally infirm persons as follows:

1. *Old Long-Stay Psychiatric Patients*
   About 40% of long-stay psychiatric patients who are now in hospital are over 65 years of age.[8] Although there is potential for rehabilitating some of these patients to enable them to take up residence in the community, it can be expected that many will spend the rest of their lives in the psychiatric hospitals. These old long-stay patients will remain the responsibility of the psychiatric service. A programme of activation and rehabilitation for these patients has been fully outlined in Chapter 10.

2. *Elderly Patients with Functional Mental Illness*
   Elderly persons suffering from functional mental illness constitute

G

about 80% of all elderly admissions to psychiatric hospitals.[10] The primary need of these patients is for psychiatric assessment, diagnosis and treatment as out-patients or in-patients.

3. *Elderly Patients with Dementia*
   Patients with dementia can be sub-divided into two groups: persons with dementia and with no significant physical illness; and persons with dementia combined with significant physical illness.

The first group consists mainly of ambulant, demented patients without severe behavioural disorder. The care of these persons does not require any input from the psychiatric service. A small number however, do exhibit serious behavioural disturbance which requires treatment by a consultant psychiatrist. The patients in the second group consist essentially of non-ambulant demented patients whose treatment needs can best be met by the geriatric medical service.

11.11   We are convinced that the medical needs of the majority of demented elderly persons should be met by the primary care service or by the geriatric medical services, with psychiatric support for patients who develop serious behavioural difficulties. We recommend that the current practice of routinely admitting demented patients to psychiatric hospitals should be discontinued. This policy has had the effect of diverting attention from the need to develop appropriate geriatric services. A comprehensive integrated geriatric service is required to cater for the needs of the elderly, including the demented elderly. This service should incorporate assessment facilities and long-stay accommodation in addition to a wide range of community support. Current policy in relation to the care of elderly persons is based on the Care of the Aged Report[11] which was published in 1968. We consider that there is an urgent need to review this policy in the light of developments which have taken place since then and to develop a comprehensive set of planning guidelines for the geriatric service for the future.

11.12   While the classification of patients which is given in paragraph 11.10 is useful for defining the area of responsibility of the psychiatric service, it is possible that borderline cases will arise. In such cases it is important to give primary consideration to the needs of the patient. We consider it appropriate to quote from the guidelines of the Royal College of Psychiatrists on collaboration between geriatricians and psychiatrists in the care of the elderly in this regard:

1. "Services for the elderly should be a unity for 'consumers' (i.e. patients, families, referrers). Patients should not be bounced back from one part of the service merely because they seem more appropriate for another part; such re-distribution of referrals should be the internal responsibility of the service.

2. 'Unity' does not mean blurring of the specificity of particular professions and facilities within the service and the patient's right of access to them.

3. Criteria for division of responsibility must be clear, and must be known and accepted both inside and outside the service.

4. Effective collaboration depends on mutual confidence, and often frankly on personal friendships. Trust is indispensable, and people should be able at times to accept each other's judgements about their own responsibilities."[12]

Prevention of Psychiatric Illness in Old Age

11.13   Coping with the high prevalence of disabling conditions in old age, including multiple disability, locomotor problems, mental deterioration and sensory disabilities, is a marked challenge to the health services. The prevention of disability requires a range of joint activities by the health and social services at various levels, both lay and professional. Co-operation between key figures in the community and health personnel is of primary importance in identifying persons at risk and in setting up preventive programmes. General practitioners have a vital role to play in secondary prevention, that is the recognition of illness and initiation of treatment at the earliest possible stage to reduce the risk of chronic disability. A World Health Organisation meeting in 1982 on services to prevent disability in the elderly has recommended:

—that screening programmes for the elderly be developed;

—that early detection and intervention policies be implemented;

—that ways be found to develop communication and links between primary health care, institutions and other major elements in the service system, including self-help groups;

—that member states promote the organisational model of the primary health care team which worked best in the local community and was designed to identify the needs of the elderly.[13]

11.14   Official policy on treatment services for the elderly should ensure that elderly persons remain in their own homes for as long as reasonably possible and that their normal lifestyle is disrupted as little as possible. To this end it is necessary to develop a comprehensive preventive programme which will prepare people for old age and help them to retain their independence. Important components of a preventive programme include:

—suitable housing, including sheltered housing

—support from voluntary organisations

—home nursing

—home helps

—meals-on-wheels

—dietary advice

—neighbourly support.

This preventive programme should actively involve the community services, particularly social and primary health care workers. Assistance from the specialised psychiatric or geriatric service should be readily available and the programme should be backed up by educational activities such as lectures and discussion groups. Health education programmes should be used to promote a healthy lifestyle and to encourage the elderly to make an active contribution to the life of their community. This will involve gaining acceptance of a more active role for the elderly in society.

11.15 Important work relevant to the aged is being carried out by the National Council for the Aged. This Council was set up in 1981 to advise the Minister for Health on all aspects of the welfare of the aged. It has produced reports on various subjects including day hospital care, retirement, community services, rural life and incomes in relation to the elderly.[14, 15, 16, 17, 18, 19] We consider that the work of the Council in exploring issues which affect the quality of life for the aged is important in terms of the contribution it makes to preventing the onset of mental infirmity in old age.

Support for Families

11.16 Where an elderly mentally infirm person is being cared for by his or her family, it is important to ensure that the family does not become overburdened. Home care can be quite successful provided that increasing support is available as the patient's disability advances and the demands made on the family become correspondingly greater. When services for the elderly are under pressure, elderly persons living alone tend to be given priority and it is often assumed that family carers can cope without any support. The absence of support from the professional services can result in a gradual wearing down of the caring relatives to the point where a minor deterioration in the patient's condition may result in his or her admission to a long-stay institution, often long before this is really necessary. It is essential that professional help should be readily available to families in the event of a crisis occurring. Support to families on a more regular basis should also be provided as the major problem for the family looking after a mentally infirm old person is the continuous nature of their responsibility. In addition to encouragement and psychological support, the family should be given periods of relief from the physical task of caring. We suggest that different methods of providing support to families might be tried out. These methods might include supports such as day care, arranging for a day or night sitter to look after the patient at home occasionally so that the family can go out, and admitting the patient regularly for short periods to a geriatric home.

Assessment

11.17   Assessment usually follows a request for the examination of an elderly person who presents a medical or social problem. Ideally, the general practitioner and the community care team should already know the elderly person and his family. However, it is probable that the majority of requests for assessment relate to persons who have not previously been receiving continuous care. The requests, therefore, come unexpectedly and often follow a crisis involving the person's family or neighbours. Assessment should always be carried out, in the first instance, at primary care level by the general practitioner and the community care team. In this context, there is an urgent need to train primary care workers in the identification and treatment of depression and in establishing the causes of confusion in elderly people since professionals often fail to identify functional mental illness among elderly persons living at home.

11.18   Wherever possible, we consider that assessment should be carried out in the patient's own home by the general practitioner. If the patient's condition cannot be entirely dealt with by his or her own doctor, referral to an out-patient clinic for consultation with the appropriate medical specialist should be the next step. However, it must be borne in mind that old people often find it difficult to get to out-patient clinics. In these circumstances, a visit to the patient's home by specialised personnel for assessment purposes may be necessary. The personnel concerned would include the psychiatric nurse, psychiatric social worker, the psychiatrist and where such specialists exist, as in large cities, the psychogeriatrician. In a minority of cases, the diagnostic facilities of the general hospital will be necessary in order to carry out a full assessment.

11.19   There are geriatric assessment units in existence in some general hospitals in this country. As elderly people can often suffer from both physical and mental illness it is recognised that elderly patients should be jointly assessed by both geriatricians and psychiatrists. In England various models of a psychiatric service for the elderly have been developed including the establishment of special psychogeriatric assessment units in some general hospitals. Under this model one or more consultant psychogeriatricians provide complete cover for all the psychiatric needs of the elderly. While psychogeriatric assessment units do not exist at present in this country, an Eastern Health Board group on psychogeriatrics has recommended the development of three such units on a pilot basis in general hospitals in the Eastern Health Board area. It is envisaged that the joint assessment units would be under the control of a psychiatrist with a special interest in the elderly and that they would be staffed by dual-trained nurses. The service provided by these units should be short-stay and they should be linked in with a network of other services including general practitioner, community-care, geriatric and psychiatric services.

Pattern of Services for the Elderly

11.20   Services for the disabled elderly are poorly developed in this country at present. Geriatric physicians are few in number and psychiatrists specialising in the care of the elderly mentally disabled are extremely rare. If general practitioner and community care services for the elderly are to operate effectively, they need to work closely with the appropriate hospital services. However, comprehensive, integrated care programmes for the elderly have not yet evolved. The disabled elderly present a special problem in urban areas. Inappropriate institutional placement of geriatric patients takes place, often as a result of social emergencies. No one service has the capacity to deliver a total care system for the disabled elderly and the available resources are poorly co-ordinated.

Appointment of Psychogeriatricians

11.21   We do not think that there is as yet any definitive model for the delivery of care for the elderly mentally infirm. The recent recognition by the Royal College of Psychiatrists of psychogeriatrics as a specialty should be helpful in delineating the contribution of psychiatry to this problem. We believe that in the larger cities a case exists for the appointment of psychogeriatricians. They would be attached to the psychiatric service and their main contribution should be:

1. to provide specialist assessment and treatment services for the elderly mentally ill,

2. to support geriatric physicians and Directors of Community Care in the development of comprehensive services for the elderly,

3. to act as a specialist resource for consultation by psychiatrist colleagues, and

86

4. to plan and co-ordinate services for the elderly mentally infirm in their area.

We suggest that the number of such posts should be small, perhaps, three in the Dublin area. In the light of experience gained, similar posts might be considered elsewhere. Outside the cities we recommend that each sector psychiatrist should provide the necessary psychiatric input to the assessment and treatment of the elderly mentally infirm in his sector.

Liaison Psychiatry

11.22   The availability of a psychiatric liaison service gives patients from the medical and surgical wards access to psychiatric consultation and should facilitate the recognition of psychiatric illness in the elderly. It also cultivates an awareness of the psychological needs of the elderly in the medical and nursing professions throughout the hospital. We consider that the provision of a consultation service by psychiatrists within the general hospital, as recommended in paragraph 7.11, is of particular relevance to the treatment of elderly patients. An effective psychiatric liaison service would provide an alternative to a psychogeriatric assessment unit in a general hospital.

Treatment and Rehabilitation

11.23   Specialist psychiatric care is only one component in the spectrum of care required for elderly mentally infirm persons. Many of these persons will be living with or near their families and much of the treatment and rehabilitation required will be provided by day care facilities and specialist out-patient services. In particular, we wish to stress that the psychiatric service for the elderly should be part of a sectorised and community-oriented service. However, to the extent that hospital care of a short-stay or medium-stay nature may be required, provision has been made in the planning ratio of 0.5 beds per 1,000 total population for short-stay and medium-stay patients, as recommended in paragraph 7.16.

New Long-stay Patients aged 65 or Over

11.24   Institutional provision will have to be made for a number of elderly persons who will need continuous care from the psychiatric service. These new long-stay elderly patients will be mainly persons who are suffering from functional mental illnesses such as schizophrenia. There will also be a small number of persons with severe dementia and serious behaviour disturbance whose condition will make it necessary for them to have continuous nursing care in the psychiatric service.

Number of Beds required for New Long-stay Patients aged 65 or Over

11.25   In considering the bed provision required for new long-stay elderly persons it is useful to look at some of the available evidence:

1. Experience in St. Davnet's Hospital, Monaghan suggests a bed provision for new long-stay patients aged 65 or over of the order of 2.4 beds per 1,000 population aged 65 or over, about one-third of this provision being for patients with dementia.

2. Data from St. Loman's Psychiatric Hospital, Dublin indicate that the estimated number of beds required for this class of patient would be about 2.2 beds per 1,000 population aged 65 or over.

3. A Department of Health and Social Security (London) planning document of 1981 forecasts a bed norm for new long-stay psychiatric patients aged over 65 of about 2.3 beds per 1,000 population aged 65 of over for 1991.[20]

11.26   In the light of this evidence we suggest a tentative estimate of 2.5 beds per 1,000 population aged 65 or over (or about 0.3 beds per 1,000 total population) for new long-stay patients aged 65 or over. This should be the upper limit of requirements. Two-thirds of this provision would relate to patients with functional mental illness and one third to patients with dementia. As in the case of the other bed norms which have been suggested in Chapter 7, we appreciate the approximate nature of this estimate and recommend that, as the new pattern of service begins to take shape, it should be closely monitored and adjusted as necessary.

11.27   The question arises as to where these continuing care beds should be located. The great majority of these patients require continuous nursing care. They do not need the diagnostic and treatment facilities of the general hospital. The location of continuing care beds for the elderly mentally infirm has been considered by a special group of geriatricians and psychiatrists in the Eastern Health Board area. Their conclusion is that these units should be based in the community. We are in general agreement this approach. The units should be independent of existing hospitals and the availability of land at a hospital should not determine the location. The majority of these elderly new long-stay patients will be suffering from severe forms of functional mental illness and we consider that these patients should be accommodated in the same high support hostels which we have recommended in Chapter 7 for the new long-stay patients aged under 65 years. Elderly new long-stay patients who are demented and disturbed should be accommodated in separate small units where continuous nursing care is available. This accommodation should be separate from that used for demented persons who are not disturbed but both sets of accommodation should be located close together in a geriatric setting. This group of patients will need the close co-operation of the psychiatrist and the geriatrician. We urge that units for new long-stay patients aged 65 or over be proceeded with as a matter of priority since many mentally infirm old people are inappropriately accommodated at present in buildings designed for other purposes such as fever hospitals and sanatoria.

11.28   The increase in the number of people surviving into advanced old age, that is 75 years and over, and the high incidence of mental illness in this age-group, is a problem not only for the psychiatric service but for the health services in general. We consider that the way in which resources are organised to meet this development should be kept constantly under review and re-assessed as the results of new research and experimentation with different models of care become available.

11.29   **Recommendations**

1. **Old long-stay psychiatric patients, elderly patients with functional mental illness and demented persons with severe behavioural disturbance, should be the responsibility of the psychiatric service (para. 11.10)**

2. **The majority of persons suffering from dementia should be cared for by the primary care service or by the geriatric service. The current practice of routinely admitting demented patients to psychiatric hospitals should be discontinued (para. 11.11)**

3. **Current policy on the care of elderly persons should be reviewed and a comprehensive set of planning guidelines for the geriatric service for the future should be drawn up (para. 11.11).**

4. **The primary care services should play an important part in the prevention of psychiatric illness in old age (para. 11.13).**

5. **A preventive programme to ensure that elderly persons remain active for as long as possible in their own homes should be implemented (para. 11.14).**

6. **Support should be given by the professional services to families who are caring for elderly mentally infirm relatives (para. 11.16).**

7. **Consideration should be given to the many possibilities for assessing elderly persons. These include assessment at primary care level, at out-patient clinics, domiciliary assessment by a member of the psychiatric team and assessment in the general hospital (para.s 11.17 to 11.19).**

8. In general, the psychiatric needs of the disabled elderly should be met by the sector team but, in densely populated areas, consideration should be given to the appointment of a psychiatrist whose main area of expertise would be the psychiatry of old age (para. 11.21)

9. Liaison psychiatry for elderly patients should be encouraged in general hospitals (para. 11.22)

10. The planning norm for accommodation for new long-stay psychiatric patients aged 65 or over should be set at 2.5 beds per 1,000 population aged 65 or over. This would equate roughly to a provision of about 0.3 beds per 1000 total population. Two-thirds of this provision should be in high support hostels for elderly persons with functional mental illness and one-third in separate small nursing units for elderly persons who are demented and who have severe behavioural disturbance (para. 11.26).

11. Elderly new long-stay patients with functional mental illness should be accommodated in the same high support hostels as new long-stay patients aged under 65 years. Elderly new long-stay patients, who are demented and who have severe behavioural disturbance should be accommodated in separate small units where continuous nursing care is available (para. 11.27).

12. The provision of accommodation in the community for elderly new long-stay patients should be proceeded with as a matter of priority (para. 11.27).

13. Services for the "older elderly" (75 years and over) group should be subject to ongoing review in the light of research and experimentation with different models of care (para. 11.28).

Chapter 12

Services for Children and Adolescents

Introduction

12.1   While the childhood origin of adult relationship and behavioural patterns has long been recognised, child psychiatry as a specialty within the medical field evolved only in the latter half of the 19th century. It has been closely linked with child neurology, developmental paediatrics, community medicine, and mental handicap. As a specialty, it has increasingly focused on prevention and early intervention, and has developed a broad community orientation.

12.2   The multidisciplinary approach to child psychiatric practice was adopted in the first child guidance clinics, which were established by William Healy in the United States in the early years of this century. These clinics with a nucleus of child psychiatrist, child psychologist, and psychiatric social worker were soon set up in many European countries, and by 1927 those in the United Kingdom were co-ordinated by the Child Guidance Council. By the 1930's child psychoanalysts had demonstrated that play was a natural investigative and therapeutic medium of great potential. In that and subsequent decades the upsurge of interest in the behavioural sciences as well as child psychiatric research, contributed greatly to theory and established a scientific base for practice. This pattern has continued, with an intensification of child psychiatric research and expertise and the incorporation of contributions from new fields of study such as psycho-linguistics, ethology and systems theory.

12.3   These developments have been paralleled by a growth in the variety of professionals treating children with problems. In addition to child psychiatrists and paediatricians, there are educational and clinical psychologists, social workers, remedial teachers, nurses, speech therapists, child psychotherapists, educational welfare officers, probation officers, play group leaders, occupational therapists and art therapists. While these specialists may work in a variety of settings there is a general acceptance of the crucial importance of co-ordination of the services they provide.

12.4   Traditionally in Irish families a high value has been placed on education and on helping children to realise their potential. In recent years more attention has been focused on the quality of children's lives. This has led to an increasing demand for appropriate support and advisory services, and for specialised help for children with difficulties. Up to recently, child and adolescent psychiatric services have developed here in an unplanned way. Services are largely concentrated in Dublin and Galway while there is no provision in many parts of the country.

12.5   The Commission of Inquiry on Mental Illness, 1966,[1] made enlightened recommendations in relation to child and adolescent psychiatric services, some of which have been implemented. In the main, our recommendations are in line with those of the Commission, allowing for the demographic changes and the developments in child psychiatry which have taken place since it reported.

The Scope of Child Psychiatry

12.6   Child and adolescent psychiatry caters for children from birth until they reach the age at which second level education normally finishes. The majority of the children treated are not mentally ill in the sense in which this term is used for adults and, in consequence, the treatment centres are usually described as child guidance clinics, family guidance clinics or child and family centres. A broad definition of the conditions involved is "abnormality of behaviour, emotions or relationships . . . sufficiently marked and sufficiently prolonged to cause handicap to the child himself and/or distress or disturbance in the family or community".[2]

12.7   Childhood emotional difficulties become evident in many ways. While there are some children with definable mental illness, in the great majority of cases the symptoms reflect an interaction of factors specific to the individual child. A diagnostic list would include childhood anxiety and phobias; depression and compulsive disorders; conduct disorders including truancy, stealing and running away from home; developmental delays and disorders; habit disorders; hyperactive children; children with psychosomatic disorders and some with specific educational disorders associated with emotional problems. There is also a small number of children with psychotic disorders, including autism and childhood schizophrenia. However, no list of conditions can encompass the range of emotional distress, damaging relationships and impaired capacity to achieve potential which characterise the young people and their parents who are seen at child and family psychiatric centres.

12.8   Children are best understood in their everyday environment of home and school, and assessment and treatment should be carried out in these settings. The practice of child psychiatry, therefore, is based in the family and community, and admission to residential settings is rarely necessary.

Prevalence of Childhood Emotional Disorders

12.9   There have been no epidemiological surveys of the prevalence of child psychiatric disorders in this country, except for childhood autism.[3] In the United Kingdom estimates of the proportion of children in the community suffering from psychiatric disorders (including maladjustment) range from 5%[4] to 18%.[5] The variation has been attributed to differing ascertainment procedures[2] as well as to regional variations.[6] In the rural community of the Isle of Wight[2] a prevalence of 6.8% was reported in 10 to 11 year old children, whereas in the London borough of Camberwell the rate was doubled, using the same survey techniques.[7] We have no reason to believe that prevalence in Ireland differs greatly from that in the United Kingdom and it is likely that the urban/rural differences are similar. However, in view of the greater proportion of children in our population, it is likely that the number with emotional problems relative to the total population is greater in Ireland than in the United Kingdom.

Prevention

12.10   By the nature of its work, child psychiatry is preventive and its emphasis is on early intervention. The child psychiatric team also undertakes direct preventive work through liaison, consultation and intervention in a variety of settings, for example:

—by working with the staff of maternity hospitals advising them on the identification of "at-risk" parents and on how to support parents of stillborn children or children who are severely ill;

—by giving guidance on good child rearing practice to the community in general and to key professionals;

—by providing a liaison psychiatric service to staff and to children and their families in a variety of medical settings such as paediatric units or general medical and surgical wards. Up to recently, the emotional needs of many hospitalised children frequently went unrecognised with the result that some children acquired additional emotional and adjustment problems;

—by treating children from broken or unhappy marriages. These children are particularly at risk of developing emotional and relationship problems and may require specialist psychotherapeutic help;

—by providing a consultation service to child residential centres;

—by providing a consultation service to the courts and to detention centres in the case of young offenders;

—by advising the community care teams on specialised areas such as child abuse, adoption and fosterage;

—by co-operating with the general psychiatric service particularly with regard to the emotional needs of children whose parents are mentally ill. In families where there is more than one patient, new approaches in family therapy warrant increased consideration;

—by adopting a wider preventive role in the community generally through participation in health education programmes in schools and liaison with teachers, probation officers, youth club leaders and other people who work with children.

Diagnosis and Early Intervention

12.11   There is considerable potential for overcoming the emotional problems of childhood if the nature of the problem is detected in time and appropriate corrective action taken. The two places in which these problems can most easily be recognised are the home and the school. In the home, parents will continue to play the central role and their capacity for identifying problems and referring them for attention must be developed. The family doctor and the public health nurse, through their professional expertise and their access to the family circumstances, are well placed to recognise when intervention may be required. We consider that the training of general practitioners and of public health nurses should have a greater emphasis on psychology to help them recognise a developing emotional problem and to take appropriate action. In addition, we recommend that at least one of the medical schools consider establishing an academic Child and Adolescent Psychiatric Department to encourage training and research.

12.12   At school, the main scope for early detection of emotional problems is in the primary classes. Teachers are in a key position to identify children with emotional problems which may be the result of factors in the home. Teachers have an important preventive role in ensuring that children with a learning disability are identified as early as possible so that appropriate measures can be taken before secondary emotional difficulties develop. The staff involved in school medical examinations should be fully aware of the potential for successful treatment of these problems if they are identified in time and examinations should be sensitive to the possibility of such problems existing. Ideally, there should be a comprehensive school psychological service at primary school level and the psychologists, irrespective of whether they are employed by the education authorities or the health authorities, should form part of the child guidance teams.

The Child Guidance Team

12.13   A typical child guidance team comprises the child psychiatrist, child psychologist and the family social worker. Depending on local circumstances, various ratios of these professional workers have been recommended.[8] The membership of the child guidance team is a matter for the employing authority, having regard to local circumstances. If the team is responsibile for school psychological work, the psychological input to the team has to be increased.

12.14   The Royal College of Psychiatrists' recommendations on staffing are as follows:

> "We have come to the conclusion that at an irreducible minimum we need two child and adolescent psychiatrists for a population of 200,000. . . . . .We consider that a realistic desirable level should be three per 200,000 population. However, the staffing of regional and supra-regional units needs to be additional to this suggested allocation"[9]

We recommend that these ratios should be taken as guidelines for this country. However, as there are no services whatever in some parts of Ireland we must plan the development of our services in a phased way. In the first instance we recommend that each health board should develop one child guidance team per 200,000 population. In health board areas where two teams are set up we recommend that one of them should develop a special interest in adolescent psychiatry. The present provision of child psychiatric services in each health board area is outlined in Appendix 5.

12.15   We recommend that there should be at least one child and family guidance centre in each health board area which would serve as the team's headquarters and where children referred could be assessed and treated as out-patients and day-patients. The child guidance team would also hold regular clinics in health centres and county clinics throughout the region. Little by way of drugs or equipment is required in these centres since milieu therapy is the main method of treatment. Consideration should therefore be given to good design and furnishings to facilitate the clinical work in these units. In particular, attention should be given to the design of eating and living accommodation and to playrooms and group therapy rooms with the incorporation of audio-visual systems as required. Child and family guidance centres do not always have to be purpose-built and it has been found that residential premises can be modified satisfactorily.

12.16   The team should also be associated with a general hospital. For some cases the child psychiatrist needs ready access to medical diagnostic facilities and consultation with paediatric, medical and other specialist colleagues. The team should develop close links with the paediatric department of the hospital. It should also be associated with the adult psychiatric department to meet the special needs of the children of psychiatric patients. The child guidance team should hold clinics in the out-patient department of the hospital. Joint child psychiatric/paediatric clinics could also be held if required.

12.17 Some health boards have arranged that outside child psychiatrists hold clinics within the region. While these provide a useful screening and referral service, they cannot provide the type of comprehensive child and family psychiatric service which we recommend.

In-Patient Services

12.18 At present there are regional in-patient units as part of the child guidance service in Dublin, Cork and Galway. This provision is in line with the recommendations of the Commission of Inquiry on Mental Illness, 1966, which also included Limerick as a centre.[1] In view of the long distances involved, we consider that small in-patient units may also be needed at other centres, for example Limerick, Sligo and Waterford. We agree with the Royal College of Psychiatrists' recommendation that consultant staffing of residential units needs to be additional to the basic allocation of psychiatrists in those areas.[9]

Services in the Eastern Health Board Area

12.19 Within the Eastern Health Board area, the rapidly expanding population and the severe social and environmental problems have resulted in a large number of highly vulnerable families where children are at considerable risk of emotional maladjustment. We agree with the general approach to developing the services which is outlined in the Eastern Health Board's report "Development of Community Mental Health Services — Planned Evolution" 1978.[10] However, there have been considerable demographic changes since this report was prepared and it would seem necessary to review current services with the aim of achieving better co-ordination and rationalisation. In addition, if our recommendations for regional services are implemented, the services in Dublin would be able to switch from providing a national to a regional service. We recommend that formal arrangements be made, involving representatives from the existing services, both health board and voluntary, to develop a co-ordinated policy for the delivery of child and adolescent psychiatric services for the area and to monitor its implementation.

96

Services for Adolescents

12.20   In paragraph 12.14 we recommended that in health boards where there are two child guidance teams, one of these should develop a special interest in adolescent psychiatry. We consider that adolescent psychiatric teams are needed urgently in the larger cities, particularly in Dublin and Cork. There is widespread public concern at the increase in disturbed behaviour among this age group. While the community as a whole should develop a wide range of social, educational and recreational facilities in response to this problem, there is also a need for specialised services. At present there are very few in-patient psychiatric facilities catering specifically for adolescents and they are usually assessed and treated by the adult service.

12.21   In the Eastern Health Board Area, there is a specialist adolescent team offering an out-patient service at Cluain Mhuire, Blackrock. We recommend that initially residential treatment facilities for adolescents be developed at Dublin, Cork and Galway. It may be that these treatment facilities can be developed in association with the existing regional child psychiatric residential units. However, clinical experience suggests that they function best as separate units with their own staff.

Community Adolescent Psychiatry

12.22   The child and adolescent psychiatric team and the specialised adolescent team, where developed, does much of its work through offering a consultation and support service to many agencies in the community. In addition, the teams see referred adolescents at community-based out-patient clinics. It has been found, however, that many adolescents are impatient with bureaucratic referral procedures, and as a result, self-referral clinics have been developed in some countries. Many of the teenagers presenting at these centres do not require highly specialised help but are in need of information, counselling and perhaps referral to the appropriate services. We recommend that "walk-in" centres should be developed in urban and suburban communities. They should be under the professional guidance of the specialist child and adolescent psychiatric service. They can be staffed by voluntary and statutory agencies from the preventive primary care service, but will need quick access to specialist opinion.

12.23   There is a growing awareness among social and other youth workers of a gap in community services for the increasing numbers of teenagers who have left home for a variety of reasons. These teenagers often sleep rough and are generally at risk. There are very few hostels where such teenagers can

H

stay. There is a need for hostels where homeless teenagers can receive shelter and guidance. These could appropriately be set up by voluntary agencies.

12.24   Conduct disorder may be a symptom of emotional disturbance or psychiatric illness. This question has been considered by the Interdepartmental Committee on Mentally Ill and Maladjusted Persons ("the Henchy Committee")[11]. Many emotionally disturbed adolescents come before the courts on various charges. We understand that the legislative procedures for juvenile offenders are being reviewed and will be incorporated in one of the proposed new Children Bills. In the interim, we recommend that the courts, particularly through their Welfare Officers, should have much greater access to child and adolescent psychiatric services for making assessments and recommendations. Where a child or juvenile requires such assessment he or she should continue to live at home unless residential assessment is required for specific purposes. In addition, where a child or juvenile charged with an offence is already attending a child guidance clinic, we recommend that any further assessment should be entrusted to that clinic unless the court considers that custodial care is required. These recommendations are in line with the Henchy Committee's recommendations 5.1 and 5.5, (IV) of its First Interim Report of August 1974.[12]

12.25   We welcome the support given by the Department of Justice to the various agencies that are developing community workshops and resource centres for adolescent offenders. We recommend that formal links be established between these centres and the local child and adolescent psychiatric service so that those with emotional problems can be identified and treated.

12.26   We welcome the present policy of regionalisation of children's homes. This will enable supportive work to continue with families and closer links to be maintained between the child and his or her family. We recommend that a similar policy for the special residential centres at Scoil Ard Mhuire, Lusk, St Laurence's, Finglas, Trinity House, Dublin and St Joseph's, Clonmel should be considered. Likewise, we recommend that these centres and the new Youth Development Centre in Dundrum should make full use of psychiatric staff not only for direct work with teenagers, but also for policy development and staff support.

Autistic Children

12.27   We have considered the special needs of autistic children. The appropriate treatment and educational services for these children have been the subject of some controversy. This has been due to a lack of knowledge of this relatively new syndrome and, in particular, insufficient information concerning treatment approaches and prognosis.

98

12.28   Childhood autism, as a distinct syndrome, was first described by Leo Kanner in 1943.[13] Since then there has been widespread discussion about the aetiology and natural history of the condition, which has at times caused confusion. The earlier psychogenic hypothesis, which implied that the condition was a reaction to the quality of parenting, is fortunately no longer upheld. It has also been shown that childhood autism is not a childhood version of adult schizophrenia.[14,15] There is now an awareness that the condition is primarily of organic origin and is associated with language disorder. The relationship between autism and mental handicap has also been researched. While autism does seriously affect the learning capacity of children, it is distinct from global mental handicap. Some autistic children are mentally handicapped as well as being autistic, but most mentally handicapped children do not have autism. While between a quarter and a third of autistic children have been shown to have an I.Q. within the normal range, they frequently do poorly on verbal tasks and on those requiring abstract thought and logic. Some of these children display special abilities in computation and at rote memory, as well as puzzle-type tests, and others can have special artistic or musical abilities.

12.29   In addition to the core of children with the classical features of childhood autism, there are others who may display only some of the features and often to a lesser extent. This is one of the reasons why there are sometimes difficulties in establishing early diagnosis causing distress to some parents. The group of children displaying autistic features can include children with sensory impairments as well as some mentally handicapped children and others with whom satisfactory channels of communication have not been established. The prevalence of childhood autism in Ireland appears to be the same as that for other countries i.e. between 2.5 and 4 per 10,000 children.[3] The male to female ratio of the condition is approximately four to one.

12.30   It is important that childhood autism is diagnosed at an early stage so that treatment can get under way. Children in whom the condition is suspected should be referred to a centre familiar with the syndrome and which has access to specialised medical and psychological investigative procedures. Assessment requires a multidisciplinary approach and, following diagnosis, therapy can be started.

12.31   Treatment requires the establishment of a relationship with the child within which learning can occur. Regular skilled counselling sessions are held with family members, and parents are regarded as co-therapists. As the child gets older, he or she meets other members of the therapeutic team, such as the remedial teacher and speech therapist. The syndrome is severely incapacitating and special educational and treatment facilities are almost always required, in many cases on a residential basis. Programmes which are behaviourally oriented have to be developed for each individual child, requiring a high staff/child ratio.

12.32   In some areas, treatment services have been developed by psychiatrists specialising in mental handicap, and in others by child psychiatrists. It is demanding and painstaking work and requires a sensitive awareness of the emotional reactions on the part of families during various phases of the child's development. Some of the children may have their educational needs met in special schools for the mentally handicapped and in time some, with support, may be able to move to ordinary classes in national schools. However, a considerable number continue to require intensive treatment and care during adolescence and adult life. The resources of the treating centres, therefore, have to include provisions for social skills and vocational training as well as sheltered workshops and recreational facilities.

12.33   There has been some discussion of the service appropriate to treating children with autism and similar conditions. The environment necessary is similar to that obtaining in many mental handicap centres. As long as the appropriate resources are provided by way of staff and facilities, it would seem immaterial whether they are developed by child psychiatrists or by specialists in mental handicap. In some cases it may be appropriate to individual children's needs to share resources, underlining the need for flexibility and good liaison between the two services. We recommend that each health board should assess the services it has available for autistic children. Following this review, a plan for the development of a comprehensive service should be drawn up. Each health board will need to decide whether this service should be provided by the mental handicap or child psychiatric service or whether an adequate level of service would best be provided by utilising the resources of both specialties.

Third Level Students

12.34   While the psychiatric needs of third level students are normally met by adult psychiatric units, it is appropriate to deal with the needs of this group in this chapter. Third-level students have a tendency to conceal or explain away psychiatric symptoms. The reluctance to seek expert help can have particularly severe effects because of the impairment of intellectual work caused by even a slight emotional disability. It is hard to form an accurate estimate of the numbers of students so affected because of mislabelling (some are thought to be academic failures) and a well-intentioned conspiracy to conceal emotional illness and treatment. Nevertheless, a widely accepted, if conservative, estimate of the proportion of students requiring professional

100

help is 14%.[16] Working from various data available, Farnsworth[17] estimated that for every 10,000 students:

—1,000 will have emotional conflicts of sufficient severity to warrant professional help;

—300 to 400 will have feelings of depression severe enough to impair their efficiency;

—100 to 200 will be apathetic and unable to organise their efforts — "I can't make myself want to work";

—20 to 50 will be so adversely affected by past family experiences that they will be unable to control their impulses;

—15 to 25 will become ill enough to require treatment in a mental hospital;

—5 to 20 will attempt suicide, of whom one or more will succeed.

12.35   Most Irish universities have a psychiatrist attached to the student health service. We consider that this arrangement should be extended to all third level educational establishments. The most important form of treatment for students is psychotherapy conducted either individually or in groups. This requires extensive training of therapists and is very time-consuming. Like other mentally ill patients, some students benefit from medication. Psychiatric involvement must however be broader than merely treating referred students. To prevent problems arising, the psychiatric service should attempt to change the attitudes of students and staff towards emotional problems by promoting understanding, tolerance and co-operation in the management of emotional problems. Such an approach is best pursued through consultation with all appropriate groups with the aim of creating a system for advice on, or referral of, emotional problems, co-ordinating and integrating counselling services within the college and improving relations between students and college management. One way these goals can be achieved is through the establishment of a tutorial system whereby all students have an expert adviser who is concerned with their academic performance. Regular consultation should take place between tutors and staff of the student health service. This arrangement provides an early warning system, and makes professional advice available at the earliest possible stage.

12.36   It is essential that professionals (psychiatrists, clinical psychologists and counsellors) should work as a co-ordinated team in the student health service. This facilitates consultations and allows for the service to be used to the maximum. It also makes possible the collection of information about factors causing mental disturbance and areas of greatest need.

12.37 **Recommendations**

1. The child psychiatric team should undertake direct preventive work through liaison, consultation and intervention in a variety of settings (para. 12.10).

2. The training of general practitioners and of public health nurses should place a greater emphasis on psychology so that they will be able to recognise, treat and refer where appropriate, emotional problems arising in families (para. 12.11).

3. At least one of the medical schools should consider establishing a Department of Child and Adolescent Psychiatry (para. 12.11).

4. There should be a comprehensive psychological service in primary schools and the psychologists should form part of the child guidance teams (para. 12.12).

5. The child guidance team should consist of a child psychiatrist, child psychologists and social workers in the appropriate ratio (para. 12.13).

6. The staffing ratios for child psychiatrists which have been devised by the Royal College of Psychiatrists should be taken as guidelines for this country. As a first step each health board should develop one child guidance team per 200,000 population and there should be at least one child and family guidance centre in each health board area (para. 12.14 and 12.15).

7. The child guidance team should be associated with a general hospital (para. 12.16).

8. In addition to the existing in-patient units in Dublin, Cork and Galway, small in-patient units should be provided as part of the child guidance service in Limerick, Sligo and Waterford (para. 12.18).

9. In the Eastern Health Board, representatives from the existing services, both health board and voluntary, should develop a co-ordinated policy for the delivery of child and adolescent services in the area (para. 12.19).

10. In health boards where two child guidance teams are set up, one of these should develop a special interest in adolescent psychiatry (para. 12.14 and 12.20).

11. Residential treatment facilities for adolescents should be developed at Dublin, Cork and Galway (para. 12.21).

12. "Walk-in" centres should be developed under the guidance of the child and adolescent psychiatric service (para. 12.22).

13. Hostels where homeless teenagers can receive shelter and guidance should be set up (para. 12.23).

14. We agree with the Henchy Committee's recommendations 5.1 and 5.5 (IV) in the First Interim Report in regard to assessment of emotionally disturbed adolescents coming before the courts and recommend formal links between services for juvenile offenders and the child and adolescent psychiatric service (para. 12.24).

15. Formal links should be established between community workshops and resource centres for young offenders and the local child and adolescent psychiatric service (para. 12.25).

16. The regionalisation of the special residential centres at Scoil Ard Mhuire, Lusk, St. Laurence's, Finglas, Trinity House, Dublin and St. Joseph's, Clonmel should be considered. These centres and the new Youth Development Centre in Dundrum when it comes into operation should avail of the expertise of adolescent psychiatric teams (para. 12.26).

17. Children in whom autism is suspected should be referred to a specialised centre where assessment can take place (para. 12.30).

18. Health boards should assess the services which they have available for autistic children. A plan for the development of a comprehensive service should then be drawn up (para. 12.33).

19. All third level colleges should have a psychiatrist attached to the Student Health Service (para. 12.35).

..ohol and Drug-Related ..roblems

Introduction

13.1 This chapter deals with psychiatric services for persons with alcohol-related problems (paragraphs 13.2 to 13.25) and with psychiatric services for persons with drug-related problems (paragraphs 13.26 to 13.43).

Alcohol-Related Problems

The Nature of Alcohol Problems

13.2 Until recently, the generic term "alcoholism" has been used to refer to a variety of problems resulting from alcohol abuse. However, because the word is difficult to define satisfactorily and because it suggests a particular type of alcohol problem to the exclusion of others, it is limited in what it covers. The term "alcohol-related problems", although more cumbersome, is more accurate. This term acknowledges that alcohol can cause, or at least contribute to, an assortment of social and physical problems which include public drunkenness, family violence, absenteeism, road traffic accidents, liver and heart disease and disorders of the central nervous system.

Size of the Problem

13.3 Alcohol-related problems make a heavy demand on the psychiatric services. There were over 7,000 admissions for alcohol abuse and alcoholic psychosis to our psychiatric hospitals and units in 1982,[1] which accounted for 26% of total admissions. The number of patients with alcohol-related problems resident in psychiatric hospitals and units on 31st March 1981 was 688 or about 5% of all resident patients.[2] This disparity between the large number of admissions and the small proportion of residents emphasises the relatively short stay in hospital of such patients. The census of patients in psychiatric hospitals and units on 31st March 1981 showed that 44% of patients with

104

alcohol-related problems had been in hospital for less than one month compared with only 8% of all other patients. Of patients admitted for alcohol abuse and alcoholic psychosis in 1982, 81% were male while the highest admission rate was in the 35-44 year age-group.

13.4 Alcohol abuse also accounts for a large number of admissions to general hospitals, for example through casualty departments as a result of traffic accidents and to general medical and surgical wards for treatment of alcohol-related illness.[3]

13.5 Alcohol-related problems also take up the time of general practitioners, social workers and the Gardai and they often lead to psychiatric disturbance in other family members. The disturbed child and the depressed spouse are the most obvious examples of this problem.

The Trend of Alcohol-Related Problems

13.6 Alcohol-related problems in Ireland have been increasing consistently and steeply in the past 15 years. In 1966 the number of admissions to psychiatric hospitals because of alcoholism was 1,757[4] or one quarter of the 1982 level. It cannot, however, be inferred that the large increase in hospital admissions reflects a corresponding increase in the prevalence of alcohol-related problems. It is likely that at least some of the increase is due to greater acceptance of the psychiatric hospital as a treatment centre for such problems. Public opinion has also increased pressure on people to seek treatment in hospital in the belief that the problems can be cured.

13.7 Other indices of alcohol-related problems, such as mortality from cirrhosis of the liver[5] and convictions for drunkenness and drunk driving,[6] have all increased during the past 15 years. Even though some of these indices, particularly the drunk driving offences conviction rate, are open to qualification, it is clear that the overall trend of alcohol-related problems in recent years has been unequivocally upwards. This is evident from Table 13.1 which shows the relationship between alcohol consumption and various indices of harm.

The Reasons for the Increase in Alcohol-Related Problems

13.8 It is now accepted that there is a close relationship between national per capita alcohol consumption and the extent of alcohol-related problems. This is certainly borne out by recent Irish experience. Since 1950 there has been an approximate doubling of alcohol consumption in Ireland — from 4.7 litres of 100 per cent alcohol per person aged 15 and over in 1950 to 9.0 in 1982.[7] The most likely explanation for this increase is the growth in disposable

TABLE 13.1

Relationship between Alcohol Consumption and Various Indices of Harm.

	Consumption: litres of 100 per cent alcohol per head of population aged 15 or over	Drunkenness: Number of prosecutions for drunkenness per 100,000 persons aged 15 or over	Cirrhosis Deaths: Death rate per 100,000 population aged 15 and over	Admissions to Psychiatric Hospitals and Units Number of admissions with a Primary Diagnosis of Alcoholism or Alcoholic Psychosis
1950	4.7	152.0	2.9	
1951	4.9	151.0	2.8	
1952	5.2	152.0	3.3	
1953	4.5	163.0	2.2	
1954	4.7	143.0	2.3	
1955	4.7	151.0	3.2	
1956	4.8	157.0	3.3	
1957	4.7	137.0	3.1	
1958	4.5	120.0	3.6	
1959	4.4	118.0	3.1	
1960	4.6	121.0	2.9	
1961	5.2	133.0	3.4	
1962	5.7	135.0	4.1	
1963	5.5	163.0	3.2	
1964	5.8	177.0	3.9	
1965	6.1	188.0	4.5	1638
1966	6.1	176.0	2.9	1757
1967	6.1	178.0	3.8	2013
1968	6.4	179.0	4.6	2526
1969	6.8	158.0	5.1	2886
1970	7.4	144.0	4.8	3073
1971	7.5	163.0	3.6	3720
1972	8.2	161.0	5.4	4143
1973	8.8	218.0	5.1	4846
1974	9.7	178.0	5.6	5355
1975	10.2	183.0	4.5	6003
1976	10.1	176.0	5.6	6101
1977	10.5	221.0	4.7	6765
1978	11.3	221.0	5.4	7293
1979	10.3	220.0	4.3	7158
1980	10.0	207.0	5.6	7021
1981	9.4	202.0	4.8	7345
1982	9.0	197.0	4.3	7189

Source: Medico-Social Research Board (Unpublished)

personal income in Ireland over the same period. This belief is supported by the downturn in alcohol consumption since 1979 when there was a simultaneous fall in disposable income. There has also been a decline in alcohol-related problems during this period. Mortality from cirrhosis of the liver[5] and convictions for drunken driving[6] have decreased since 1979. Admissions to psychiatric hospitals and units for alcohol abuse and alcoholic psychosis

106

decreased from 7,293 in 1978[8] to 7,021 in 1980.[9] The number of admissions increased slightly again in 1981 to 7,345 and in 1982 the figure was 7189.[10]

The Management of Alcohol-Related Problems in Ireland

13.9   The traditional response in Ireland to alcohol-related problems has been predominantly treatment-oriented and it is only recently that preventive measures such as health education have gained prominence. In international public health circles on the other hand, the emphasis has passed from treatment to prevention. This is reflected in the first recommendation of a World Health Organisation Expert Committee Report on "Problems Related to Alcohol Consumption" (1980):

> "In view of the wide diversity of medical and social ills and human suffering resulting from the consumption of alcoholic beverages, the limited efficacy and high cost of the existing treatment and management of most of these problems, and their high prevalence in many parts of the world, the Committee recommends that (a) prevention should be given clear priority; (b) further investment in treatment should be concentrated on developing inexpensive cost-effective services".[11]

13.10   Recent trends in Ireland in the management of alcohol-related problems have been towards greater specialisation, often involving costly in-patient care which has tended to separate the treatment and management of alcohol-related problems from community medical and social services. The wisdom of this approach is questionable on at least two grounds:

1. The effectiveness of specialised alcohol treatment programmes has been seriously questioned.[12] There is no evidence that intensive, high-cost in-patient treatment is in any way superior to simple, inexpensive community-based intervention. Compared with the latter form of management, the intensive approach is not considered to be cost effective.[13]

2. The over-specialised approach to alcohol-related problems is also a separatist approach. It draws the problem away from the community and family and tends to exclude the contribution of primary care and community medical and social services from the management of the problem. To that extent, it runs counter to the general principles of the delivery of health care which stress that help to individuals and families should be as near to their communities and homes as possible.

Prevention

13.11   In accordance with World Health Organisation opinion, we believe that in future the emphasis should be on prevention rather than treatment of alcohol-related problems. We acknowledge that prevention must involve a multi-faceted approach which is integrated, co-ordinated and comprehensive. We recommend that consideration should be given to appropriate preventive measures such as:

—higher taxation of alcohol and ensuring that the real price of alcohol is not reduced by inflation

—stricter enforcement of the laws against drunken driving and under-age drinking

—restrictions on drink advertising

—restrictions on availability of alcohol.

We recognise that the effectiveness of such measures is open to debate[7] and that the drawing up of an appropriate policy is a complex matter. In paragraph 13.25 we recommend that an inter-departmental body should be set up in order to establish a national alcohol policy.

13.12   We emphasise the importance of the general practitioner's function in the prevention of alcohol-related problems. This is referred to in the recent Report of the Working Party on the General Medical Service:

"The general practitioner is also in a position to identify cases of alcohol dependence in his practice, directly and through the care of the alcoholic's family. He is thus in a position to intervene in a major source of physical, mental and social hardship in the community".[14]

Health Education

13.13   Preventive approaches to alcohol-related problems have focused largely on health education which has tended to concentrate on the repetition of messages to young people on the dangers of alcohol. Experts now agree that such an approach, although it may be useful in informing persons, is less effective in influencing their behaviour.[15] We consider it important that teachers, including primary school teachers, should instruct their pupils in health education, including the healthy use of alcohol in everyday life. The Health Education Bureau is expected to develop teacher training programmes in health education and we welcome this development.

Health Promotion

13.14   It is now believed that health education, i.e. the transmission of isolated pieces of information concerning various kinds of health-damaging behaviour, cannot effectively stand on its own but must be part of a wider approach designed to influence behaviour. This wider approach is called health promotion. Essentially, health promotion consists of the promotion of health-enhancing activities and the suppression of health-damaging ones. It includes not only the actions and attitudes of individuals but also the policies and activities of industries, corporations, governments and other public authorities.

13.15   While there are limits to the extent to which interventions or prohibitions can be implemented effectively, nevertheless there would seem to be a conflict between the health education message and the apparent lack of concern about alcohol abuse as evidenced by, for example, the non-enforcement of the laws concerning under-age drinking, the recent reduction in the cost of spirits and the proposed extension of opening hours. From the health promotional point of view, we consider that a national commitment to a policy on alcohol consumption and to the implementation of that policy is essential. In the words of the 1980 WHO report referred to in paragraph 13.9:

> "there is ample evidence that the damage caused by the consumption of alcoholic beverages is closely related to the level of consumption both of individuals and of the population as a whole. Indices of alcohol-related damage, biomedical as well as social, tend to rise when per capita consumption rises."

This point is illustrated in Table 13.1. The WHO report recommended that governments should take immediate steps to prevent any further increases in consumption and should begin to reduce per capita consumption by reducing the availability of alcoholic beverages and by taking educational and other measures to reduce demand.

Importance of a Community-Based Approach

13.16   While we emphasise the fundamental importance of prevention of alcohol-related problems, we acknowledge that there are no preventive measures immediately in sight which would completely abolish the occurrence of such problems. Therefore, treatment will continue to be necessary. As far as possible, these problems should be dealt with at a community level by the primary health care and social services. One reason for this is that the problems occur in local and family settings and therefore the community-based response will be earlier. It will take into account all aspects of the drinker's immediate environment, including his family, and will therefore be comprehensive in its scope. In addition, a community-based approach is more likely to be cost-effective.

Need for a Local Alcoholism Service

13.17   Notwithstanding the considerations outlined in paragraph 13.16, there is still a need for some specialisation in the field of alcohol-related problems and we put forward the following guidelines for the development of local alcoholism services:

1. As part of a comprehensive psychiatric service, each sector should develop a local alcoholism service. This service should be community-based and the major emphasis should be on out-patient treatment.

2. The sector service should have access to a small number (2 or 3) of beds. This in-patient component might be used for patients who could not attend the out-patient service due to the long distances involved or for social reasons. The question of location should be decided locally.

3. Each hospital catchment area should arrange to have one consultant psychiatrist take special responsibility for the organisation and operation of services for persons with alcohol-related problems in the area.

4. The sector service should act as a resource centre for all the services concerned with alcohol abuse in the sector. It is important that alcoholic counsellors should get involved in educational and preventive work, for example educating people to see the contribution of alcohol to work difficulties, teaching personnel managers how to deal with employees who have alcoholic problems, lecturing local groups about the nature of alcoholism. The staff in the alcoholism service should use their expertise to support others who may in the course of their work come in contact with persons with alcohol problems and to further the prevention of alcohol abuse.

5. The psychiatric team should provide a consultation service to general practitioners and other primary health care personnel concerning the treatment and management of persons with alcohol-related problems and their families. This is particularly important in the case of general practitioners.

6. We acknowledge the major contribution made by voluntary groups such as Alcoholics Anonymous to the support and treatment of persons with alcohol-related problems. We recommend that the service provided by voluntary agencies should be integrated with the local health board service, and that there should be full co-operation and flexibility of arrangements. The nature of alcohol-related problems requires a broadly based approach to prevention and treatment. There is considerable scope for voluntary groups and members of the general public to become involved at a local level in helping persons with alcohol-related problems and their families.

Homeless Alcoholics

13.18   Special provision will be required for vagrant alcoholics. Because of excessive alcohol consumption over the years or for other reasons combined with, or separate from, alcohol consumption these people have become socially detached and homeless. This group was described in the report "Medical Services for Homeless People" as follows:

> "There is a group of people whose physical and mental health is in a state of abject ruin. Their lives revolve around a culture whose focus is cheap alcohol. Many have become timeless and spaceless. Most suffer from chronic ill-health which is rarely given constructive attention. Their life pattern oscillates from the street to the prison or casualty department and back to the street again".[16]

13.19   In their report "Homeless and Vulnerable"[17] the Simon Community estimate that there are about 3,000 homeless people in Ireland to-day. This report concludes that the homeless population suffers from an abnormally high rate of illness, far above that of the housed population. In addition to medical problems such as malnutrition, tuberculosis and bronchitis, many homeless people develop alcohol-related problems.

13.20   Even though it may not be possible to alter substantially their underlying personality and behavioural problems, there is a need to provide homeless people with shelter, food and clothing. These services are now provided by organisations such as the Simon Community. We recommend that local health and social services should strengthen their co-operation with voluntary organisations in providing care for these people. Hostels, soup-runs and other support services should be developed so that the basic living needs of these people are catered for. In addition, some homeless people will need to avail of the alcoholism service and day facilities provided by the psychiatric service.

Other Facilities for Persons with Alcohol-Related Problems

13.21   In addition to health board services for persons with alcohol-related problems, a treatment service is provided by a number of private psychiatric hospitals. The main private hospitals are St. Patrick's Hospital, Dublin, St. John of God's, Stillorgan, Co. Dublin and Belmont Park Hospital, Waterford. In 1982, there were 1,843 admissions for alcohol abuse and alcoholic psychosis to these hospitals which accounted for 26% of such admissions to all psychiatric hospitals and units.[1] In general, these hospitals, particularly the two Dublin hospitals, admit people from all over the country. The two Dublin hospitals are also paid by the Eastern Health Board to provide a local catchment area service in general psychiatry.

13.22   One disadvantage of having centralised treatment centres for alcohol-related problems is that it is not always conducive to family intervention as part of the treatment programme. In addition, the availability of these services has lessened the demand for local services. Many people prefer to be admitted to a hospital far away from their local area as they want to hide the fact that they have a drink problem.

13.23   Treatment services for persons with alcohol-related problems at private psychiatric hospitals grew mainly as a result of a demand for services which was not being met within the public psychiatric service. It is only recently that such specialised services have been developed at health board psychiatric hospitals. In view of the increasing attention by the public psychiatric service to this problem, there is a need for closer liaison between the public and private services. We recommend that the private psychiatric hospitals should be linked in with the health board's policy on alcohol-related problems and we endorse the practice whereby these hospitals provide services for the health boards on an agency basis.

Centres Set up by Voluntary Groups

13.24   In recent years a number of centres for the treatment of persons with alcohol-related problems have been set up by voluntary groups. A number of different approaches are used in these centres. It is probable that they were set up because of the lack of local services. Some of the centres receive funding from the Department of Health or from the health boards. We recommend that the services provided in these centres should be monitored and evaluated on an ongoing basis. This should include the collection of statistics on criteria for admission, numbers of patients treated, length of time in attendance at the centre, etc. so that the cost-effectiveness of the services provided can be measured.

An Inter-departmental Monitoring Group on Alcohol Consumption and Problems

13.25   Because of the involvement of alcohol in many aspects of our society ranging from trade to health, a national alcohol policy can be instigated only by an inter-departmental body, representative of all Government departments concerned. Not alone must the Department of Health be involved but also the Departments of Social Welfare, Justice, Industry, Trade, Commerce and Tourism, Environment, Labour, Finance and Education, all of which have substantial inputs into areas of responsibility concerning alcohol. The Irish

National Council on Alcoholism (I.N.C.A.) is the primary advisory body in the field of alcohol-related problems in this country, and this organisation should be involved in the formulation of a national alcohol policy. In view of the important role of Alcoholics Anonymous in the support and treatment of persons with alcohol-related problems, this organisation should also be represented. We recommend that steps be taken to set up an inter-departmental committee which will be responsible for drawing up a national alcohol policy.

Drug-Related Problems

Introduction

13.26 . Misuse and abuse of barbiturate and morphine-like drugs have been a concern of the medical profession for a long time. Until comparatively recently the problem was a circumscribed one and was generally seen among persons who, by reason of their occupation, had easy access to drugs. Doctors, pharmacists and nurses were, therefore, the persons most often affected. The use of barbiturate drugs for their sedative and hypnotic properties and amphetamines for weight-reducing during the 1950s and 1960s resulted in an increasing dependence on these drugs which at that time were freely medically prescribed. During the 1960s the abuse of drugs, barbiturates and amphetamines, particularly by young people, became relatively common. This led to the growth of preventive measures as society and the professions responded to the problem. Increasing recognition of the dependence-forming properties of barbiturates and amphetamines and of their potential for causing severe withdrawal symptoms, including psychosis, led to gradually more stringent legal safeguards being taken which limited their availability.

13.27   In Ireland, abuse of amphetamines leading to psychosis and requiring hospitalisation was first reported in 1966.[18] Two years later a Working Party on Drug Abuse was established by the Minister for Health and presented its report in 1971.[19] The Working Party attempted to review the extent of drug abuse in Ireland and concluded that in September 1969 there were approximately 350 persons abusing drugs in the Dublin area who were known to the Gardaí. This number had, by December 1970, increased to 940. Drugs most commonly abused at the later date were believed to be cannabis and lysergic acid diethylamide (LSD). The Working Party declared that there was "no evidence of any significant use of heroin". They added, however, that "the position should not be viewed with complacency". The Working Party recommended various measures: the prevention of illicit acquisition of drug supplies, control in the prescription and supply by doctors of drugs and increased education and publicity concerning the dangers of drug abuse.

Finally they made recommendations for treatment and rehabilitation of drug abusers.

13.28   In June 1969 a National Drug Advisory and Treatment Centre was opened in Jervis Street Hospital as a service to drug abusers and their families. In 1975 an in-patient detoxification unit was provided at the centre. In 1974 a Committee on Drug Education which had been set up by the Minister for Health, presented its report.[20] It recommended drug education through seminars, lectures and booklets and by local health board education teams. The Committee also indicated that evaluation of all programmes should take place.

13.29   There were also initiatives in the areas of crime-prevention and legislation. In 1968 the Garda Drug Squad was established. In 1977 the Misuse of Drugs Act became law, incorporating a comprehensive list of measures regulating possession, cultivation, importation and dissemination of specified drugs. The Misuse of Drugs Act, 1984, was introduced primarily to update the penalty provisions of the 1977 Act, and to introduce some technical amendments to that Act which would allow easier enforcement of its provisions.

13.30   In 1983 a special Government Task Force on Drug Abuse was established. Their recommendations were released in September 1983 and covered the areas of law enforcement, education, community and youth developments, health and research.[21] The Task Force considered that one of the main problems in the area of drug abuse was lack of information about what causes it and also about its true incidence in the community. Arising from the Task Force's recommendation that there should be reliable information on the drug problem, the Medico-Social Research Board was requested to carry out four research projects. The Government has also decided to establish a National Co-ordinating Committee on Drug Abuse on a formal basis which will submit a report to the Minister for Health annually. This committee will be empowered to make recommendations to the relevant Ministers and will assume responsibility for the implementation of the Task Force's recommendations.

Definition

13.31   To define a "drug" is no easy task. To say that a drug is something which alters the physiology of a metabolism is too broad because that includes, for example, water. We are mainly concerned here with drugs which affect mood or sleep. A distinction should be made between "licit" drugs (that is medically prescribed drugs or drugs for which no medical prescription is necessary), and "illicit" drugs (drugs for which a prescription is required but

114

which have not been properly prescribed by a medical practitioner for the person taking them, or drugs such as cannabis whose prescription is prohibited by law). The words "abuse and misuse" are also difficult to define. A recent W.H.O. publication commented:

> "abuse" and "misuse" are unsatisfactory concepts within a scientific approach. Because the terms involve value judgments they are impossible to define in such a way that they are appropriate for different drugs in different contexts".[22]

Although aware of the limitations of the expression, we use the global term 'drug abuse' to cover all "illicit" drug use and the use of "licit" drugs inappropriately, such as in higher dosage than prescribed or beyond their period of efficacy or necessity, whether so prescribed or not.

13.32 Drug abuse may be episodic, intermittent or continuous depending on the pattern of usage and the damage resulting. When describing abuse the drug category involved should be stipulated. This is best done on a hierarchal basis when more than one drug is involved so that a polydrug abuser taking both cannabis and opiates is classified as an opiate abuser and a cocaine and cannabis abuser is classified as a cocaine abuser.

Extent of the Problem

13.33 The Working Party on Drug Abuse reporting in 1971 was not optimistic about the potential for measuring the extent of the drug problem.[19] It declared that "there is no practical method of measuring precisely the prevalence of drug abuse in the community". Unfortunately, most of the data available to us concerning drug abuse in Ireland, as elsewhere, suffers from imprecision of definition. In addition, some of the surveys carried out tell us little concerning trends in abuse. A report by Byers[23] to the Eastern Health Board Task Force on Drug Abuse in November 1982 examined the extent and type of drug abuse prevalent in the Eastern Health Board area. This report was based on evidence from health professionals, legal sources, educational sources and voluntary organisations and concluded that drug abuse had increased in the Eastern Health Board area in the eighteen months preceding completion of the report. Surveys of school children have focused simply on whether they have been offered or have tried drugs.[24, 25] A survey in 1983[26] of an unrepresentative area of Dublin showed high drug abuse among a substantial portion of the young people in this socially deprived population. A more recent study by the Medico-Social Research Board[27] on heroin use in a Dún Laoghaire borough area estimated that 2.2% of people aged 15-24 had used heroin in the one year period under study. This percentage of heroin use was considerably lower than the corresponding 10% in the same age range reported in the Bradshaw study and the authors commented that

"This finding offers some hope that intensive local efforts, over the past year and a half, to counter experimentation with dangerous drugs among the young have not gone in vain".

13.34 Indirect evidence, however, does suggest that there has been a substantial increase in illicit drug use in Dublin in recent years. There has been a considerable increase in the numbers treated at the National Drug Advisory and Treatment Centre including many stated to be abusing heroin. For the period January to December 1983, inclusive, a total of 1,515 patients attended the Centre and 841 of these patients were new patients. Heroin was the most frequently recorded drug of abuse (1,006 cases).[28] In addition the number of convictions for drug abuse and of seizures by the Gardaí and customs officers of heroin and other drugs has greatly increased.[29] It can, therefore, be concluded that there has been a substantial increase in illicit drug use in the Dublin area.

Prevention

13.35 There are currently two approaches to prevention of drug abuse. The first of these is the law enforcement approach. This is concerned with preventing the importation of drugs such as heroin and cocaine. It also involves the detection, prosecution and conviction of "pushers" i.e. those who market the drug for profit. If the law enforcement measures are effective, this constitutes a vital preventive measure. However, there are difficulties. In many cases the Gardaí claim that, while they are aware of the identity of pushers, there is substantial difficulty in obtaining convictions.

13.36 The other approach to prevention of drug abuse is education. As in the case of alcohol, there is little solid evidence to show that school educational programmes are effective in the prevention of drug abuse. There are suggestions that they may be counter-productive by stimulating interest in drugs. In any case, heroin abusers tend to be those who leave school at 14, who are of poor intelligence and who have a record of primary school non-attendance.[25] Therefore, it appears that school programmes often do not reach the high risk group at which they should be aimed. For these reasons, we are reluctant to advocate the commitment of substantial funds to drug education programmes. However, we consider that, as in the case of education about alcohol, the contribution of teachers is important. Teachers should provide general health education in schools including the dangers of drug abuse. Education about drug abuse should take place in the context of an overall education for life programme which would cover education on both illicit drug use and the improper use of licit drugs, as well as alcohol, tobacco and other substance abuse.

Treatment Approaches

13.37   In considering therapeutic approaches to drug abuse, it must be remembered that in the case of serious abuse such as that relating to heroin, many social factors are involved. For example, drug abuse may be just a symptom of multiple community difficulties and disadvantages. Thus, centre city drug abuse is usually related to crime either directly or indirectly. While in an in-patient unit and in the short term, it may be a simple matter to withdraw a heroin addict from his dependence, keeping him abstinent is more difficult. The social network in which he exists is likely to absorb him again when he returns to it and indeed he may himself be involved in drug-related crime. For these and other reasons, the data from such specialist treatment centres as provide figures do not tell the full story. As in the case of alcohol dependence, there is no convincing evidence that highly specialised, costly and sometimes residential approaches to drug problems are cost-effective for the community as a whole. Treatment programmes which, prima facie, have good results may be dealing with only a selected part of the problem. It is questionable whether most drug abusers would derive benefit from such programmes. We consider that the Department of Health should arrange that all programmes of treatment for drug abuse should be independently evaluated as to their cost effectiveness.

Drugs and the Psychiatric Service

13.38   The 1945 Mental Treatment Act envisaged psychiatric involvement in drug abuse when it made provision for the compulsory hospitalisation of "addicts to drugs" for a maximum period of one year. However, the role of the psychiatric hospitals in this field was minimal. In 1965 there were 84 admissions to psychiatric hospitals and units in Ireland for drug addiction.[4] Yet, despite the probable increase in the drug problem in the ensuing 15 years, the number of comparable admissions in 1982 was still only 223.[1]

13.39   We consider that the sector psychiatric team has an important function in the prevention of drug abuse. This should include:

—supporting law enforcement agencies via consultation with Gardaí and prison authorities;

—education of professionals such as teachers and general practitioners;

—adopting a responsible approach through health education to avoid sensationalism about drug abuse.

13.40   In the light of the considerations set out in previous paragraphs, we would not feel justified in recommending greatly increased residential facilities

117

for treatment of drug abuse. Rather, we feel that the approach must be community-based with inputs from both medical and social personnel together with the voluntary organisations. Because of the relationship between criminality and heroin abuse, community workers will have to work closely with probation officers and the Gardaí.

13.41   We are not in favour of the treatment by general practitioners of drug addicts. We consider that the role of the general practitioner is in early detection, education and prevention and provision of follow-up services. Increased vigilance on the part of general practitioners may permit intervention before dependency has been established. General practitioners can also educate parents in the early detection of drug abuse.

13.42   The psychiatric service has an involvement in problems arising from both the illicit use of drugs and the improper use of prescribed drugs. The official classification of psychiatric disorders of the American Psychiatric Association classifies drug abuse and drug dependence as psychiatric disorders.[30] If drug abuse escalates, psychiatrists will have the main responsibility for dealing with this problem.

13.43   A cause for more immediate concern is the number of persons attending general practitioners or the psychiatric service and licitly taking prescribed psycho-active drugs, who are psychologically dependent on these drugs. The volume of prescription of sedatives and hypnotic psycho-active drugs by general practitioners is clearly evident from the General Medical Services (Payments) Board data.[31] The psychiatric service has an important role to play in preventing licit drug dependence by more careful prescribing and by the use of alternative treatment methods and in reducing the number of those already dependent.

13.44   **Recommendations**

Alcohol-Related Problems

1. **The approach to alcohol-related problems should be based on prevention rather than treatment (para. 13.11).**

2. **Health promotion should form the basis of a preventive approach to alcohol-related problems. This will involve a commitment to a national policy on alcohol consumption and the implementation of that policy (para. 13.14 and 13.15).**

3. **The emphasis in the management of alcohol-related problems should be on community-based interventions rather than on specialised in-patient treatment. This approach involves a major**

118

input from general practitioners and the social services as well as the local psychiatric service (para. 13.16).

4. Local alcoholism services should be developed in accordance with the guidelines set out in para. 13.17.

5. Health boards should co-operate with voluntary organisations in providing special services for homeless alcoholics (para. 13.20).

6. There should be closer liaison between the public and private services for persons with alcohol-related problems. Private psychiatric hospitals should be linked in with the local health board's policy on treatment and management of persons with alcohol-related problems (para. 13.23).

7. Centres for the treatment of persons with alcohol-related problems which have been set up by voluntary groups and which receive public funding should be monitored on an ongoing basis (para. 13.24).

8. A cross-sectoral body comprising representatives from all Government departments concerned with alcohol, the Irish National Council on Alcoholism and Alcoholics Anonymous should be set up to draw up a national policy on alcohol consumption and problems (para. 13.25).

Drug-Related Problems

9. Teachers should give their pupils instruction on the dangers of drug abuse as part of a wider health education programme (para. 13.36).

10. The Department of Health should arrange that all programmes of treatment for drug abuse should be independently evaluated as to their cost effectiveness (para. 13.37).

11. The psychiatric team should play an active part in the prevention of illicit drug abuse as outlined in para. 13.39.

12. The approach to the drug problem should be community-based and general practitioners, social workers and voluntary organisations have an important function in this regard. Community workers should work closely with the Gardaí (para. 13.40).

13. The psychiatric service has an important role to play in preventing licit drug dependence and in reducing the numbers of people already dependent (para. 13.43).

Chapter 14

Organisation and Management

Introduction

14.1   The development of a comprehensive community-based psychiatric service has major implications for the staffing and management of the service. The basic unit of service will be the sector team. The team should be located in the sector, involving a move away from the traditional centralisation of services in the psychiatric hospital. The primary commitment of the members of the sector team will be to the community they serve, that is to the population of the sector and not to a particular institution. There should be much more movement of staff, with members of the sector team moving freely from one service component to another to ensure continuity of care for the patient.

14.2   The services provided in a sector should include out-patient clinics, day care facilities and community residential accommodation. In some areas the day facility may be shared by a number of sector teams. In these cases, it is important that there is continuity of care and that the same psychiatric team should continue to have clinical responsibility for patients. The in-patient service, whether this is in a psychiatric or general hospital, will serve a number of sectors. This means that several psychiatric teams will share responsibility for the beds in the hospital. A number of specialised services will also be shared, for example high intensity rehabilitation programmes for old long-stay patients and educational programmes for medical and nursing staff.

Sector Team

14.3   Each sector team will be led by a consultant psychiatrist and include psychiatric nurses and an administrator. The team should have access to a psychologist, social worker and an occupational therapist. The headquarters of the sector team should be located where they do most of their work and in many cases this will be in the day facility.

120

Teamwork

14.4   The psychiatrist has ultimate clinical responsibility for the mentally ill patient and, as team-leader, has overall responsibility for the functioning of the multidisciplinary team. Each member of the team should have his or her own particular area of professional responsibility and expertise but there will be considerable overlap of roles. It is important that the members of the sector team appreciate the value of working together as a team and that they are prepared to adopt a multiprofessional approach whenever this is to the patient's benefit.

14.5   At present there is a scarcity of psychologists, social workers and occupational therapists in the psychiatric service and there is a need for health boards to expand the numbers employed. In some parts of the country at present psychologists and social workers working in the psychiatric service are part of the community care programme or the general hospital programme. This arrangement has caused problems in the co-ordination of activities by the members of the psychiatric team and in the delegation of duties. We consider that the psychologists and social workers attached to one or more sector teams should be part of the psychiatric service i.e. special hospital programme but, for promotion purposes, they should be allowed to compete with members of their own profession in other areas of the health service.

Role of Psychiatric Nurses

14.6   At present some 6,000 psychiatric nurses work in hospitals and units[1] and about 169 psychiatric nurses work outside the hospital setting. The transition from a hospital-oriented to a community-oriented psychiatric service, with a consequent reduction in the range of in-patient facilities, will entail a redeployment of nursing resources to the community. To equip them for this new role existing hospital-based nurses will require continuing training and education. They will need to acquire the knowledge and skills necessary to operate a community-based psychiatric service. Otherwise, established practices of hospital care will be transferred inappropriately into a different setting. As stated in paragraph 4.1, rather than separate "hospital nurses" and "community nurses", we recommend that nurses should be able to work in any component of a comprehensive psychiatric service. This will mean that nurses may have the opportunity to work in a hospital or community setting and may also be able to rotate from one setting to the other.

14.7   The need for psychiatric nurses to take on a more therapeutic role in the implementation of rehabilitation programmes was referred to in Chapter 10. This is a pre-requisite to moving old long-stay patients (as defined in

Chapter 7) to residential accommodation in the community. The role of the psychiatric nurse should evolve in accordance with developments in the psychiatric service. In most parts of the country, it will take some time to build up a community psychiatric service and the intervening period should be used to organise programmes of training and education for nurses. These programmes should be geared to teaching skills necessary for rehabilitation and for community work. As the in-patient component of the service declines, it should be possible to convert a number of existing posts, based solely in hospitals, into posts for paramedical and other grades, where there are few approved posts at present.

14.8   The National Union/Management Forum on psychiatric nursing is currently dealing with issues such as the status of trainee psychiatric nurses, recruitment, promotion to supervisory posts and integration of male and female staff. We consider that the immediate implementation of the agreements reached on these issues in relation to psychiatric nursing is essential to future developments in the psychiatric service.[2]

Review of Organisation of the Psychiatric Service

14.9   The organisational structure we have proposed in this report requires the continued existence of a separate health care programme for the psychiatric service. We suggest that the term Special Hospital Programme be changed to Psychiatric Programme as the present term ignores the many community facilities in the psychiatric service. We recognise that this structure has a disadvantage in that it creates a boundary between the psychiatric service and other health services. It is essential that this separation of the psychiatric service does not result in the delivery of psychiatric services in isolation from the community care service and the general hospital service. We have already emphasised that there should be close working links between the psychiatric service and general practitioner and community care services and that the in-patient service for all admissions should be provided in general hospitals. We consider that a separate programme structure for psychiatry is necessary now in order to bring about in an ordered way the major transition to the community-oriented psychiatric service we have recommended. A unified management and organisational structure for both community and in-patient services will facilitate the redeployment of resources from the hospital setting to the community service. However, when the stage is reached where most psychiatric care is being delivered in the community, we consider that the position of the psychiatric service in relation to other health service care programmes should be re-assessed.

14.10   In the meantime, community psychiatric services should be so organised that the amalgamation of these services and other community care services will be facilitated. For example, in Chapter 4 we recommended that psychiatric sectors should share the same boundaries with Community Care areas. Sectors for the delivery of psychiatric services and catchment areas for general hospital services should also be aligned with each other. In addition, the possibility of locating the psychiatric team on the same campus as a community health centre should be examined.

Catchment Area Management Committee

14.11   The term "catchment area" refers to the area served by a psychiatric hospital or general hospital psychiatric unit. Each health board will therefore contain a number of catchment areas and the catchment areas will be further sub-divided into sectors. We recommend that catchment area management committees should be set up by each health board. These committees should be representative of the sector teams in that area and should also include representatives of the local community care teams. The catchment area management committee should be chaired by a Clinical Director/Resident Medical Superintendent/Chief Psychiatrist who will have overall responsibility for the service in the catchment area.

14.12   The membership of the catchment area management committee should include the following:

—Chief Psychiatrist

—Sector Psychiatrists

—Chief Nursing Officer and sector nursing representatives

—Senior Administrator

—Senior Psychologist

—Senior Social Worker

—Senior Occupational Therapist

—Representatives of Community Care teams.

The committee should be responsible for both community and in-patient psychiatric services. It will advise on the planning and development of local services with particular regard to the transition from a hospital-oriented to a community-oriented service organised on a sector basis and the changes entailed for the psychiatric hospital. We recommend that the committee should meet at least once a month.

Chief Psychiatrist

14.13 We favour the retention of the system whereby a Chief Psychiatrist/Resident Medical Superintendent/Clinical Director is appointed on a permanent basis. However, the role of the Chief Psychiatrist will change as the pattern of services changes. We would stress the importance of good leadership by the Chief Psychiatrist and of a clear plan of priorities for the development of services. He or she will need to motivate the staff and gain their co-operation and commitment in achieving the changes required. Chief Psychiatrists/Resident Medical Superintendents/Clinical Directors should be encouraged to acquire and develop administrative skills and in particular have some familiarity with epidemiology, health economics and health planning.

Hospital Management Team

14.14 While the Catchment Area Management Committee will have an important role in relation to the development of all psychiatric services in the area, we recommend that the day-to-day management of the psychiatric hospitals should be the responsibility of a small management team in each hospital. The hospital management team should consist of:

—Chief Psychiatrist

—Senior Administrator

—Chief Nursing Officer.

14.15 **Recommendations**

1. **The services provided in a sector should include out-patient clinics, day care facilities and community residential accommodation (para.14.2).**

2. **The sector team should be multidisciplinary. The headquarters of the sector team should be where they do most of their work and in many cases this will be in the day facility (para. 14.3).**

3. **Psychologists and social workers on the sector teams should be part of the psychiatric service but, for promotion purposes, they should be allowed to compete with members of their own profession in other areas of the health service (para. 14.5).**

4. **To avoid having separate "hospital nurses" and "community nurses", nurses should be able to work in any component of a comprehensive psychiatric service (para. 14.6).**

124

5. Programmes of training and education for nurses in rehabilitation and in community work should be organised in all parts of the country (para. 14.7).

6. The term Special Hospital Programme should be changed to Psychiatric Programme (para. 14.9).

7. When the stage is reached where most psychiatric care is in the community, the organisational position of the psychiatric service in relation to other health services should be re-assessed (para. 14.9).

8. Community psychiatric services should be so organised that the amalgamation of these services and other community care services will be facilitated (para. 14.10).

9. Catchment area management committees should be set up by each health board (para. 14.11).

10. The composition and function of the catchment area management committee should follow the guidelines set out in para. 14.12.

11. The day-to-day management of the psychiatric hospitals should be the responsibility of a small management team in each hospital (para. 14.14).

Chapter 15

Cost Implications

Introduction

15.1   In drafting this report we were primarily concerned to set out an overall policy framework for the future planning and development of the psychiatric service. The main thrust of our recommendations centres on the simultaneous building up of services in the community and reduction of the current over-reliance on the psychiatric hospital. At present, the bulk of resources is spent on the psychiatric hospitals. In assessing the likely cost implications of our recommendations, it is necessary to take account of the considerable scope for redeployment of existing revenue resources which will become possible as the new pattern of services takes shape. It is also necessary to take account of the expenditure which will arise in maintaining the existing service if our recommendations are not implemented.

15.2   In looking at the funding which will be required over the coming years, a distinction should be made between the capital resources which will be needed for any new or adapted buildings and the on-going, revenue resources which will be needed to run the services envisaged in this report.

Capital Resources Required

15.3   The capital resources required will fall under the following main headings:

In-patient services for short-stay and medium-stay patients.

In-patient services for new long-stay patients.

Day facilities.

Community-based residences.

Minor capital improvement schemes.

In-patient Services for Short-stay and Medium-stay Patients.

15.4   The continued development of psychiatric units in general hospitals, which is recommended in Chapter 7, would represent the greatest single element of capital expenditure on in-patient accommodation. If all short and medium-stay bed requirements were to be located in the general hospital setting a total of about 1,700 beds would be required nationally. This figure is based on the planning guideline of 0.5 beds per 1,000 total population recommended in paragraph 7.16. At present, there are about 700 such beds available or being built outside the public psychiatric hospitals. The capital cost of providing the balance of 1,000 beds is estimated to be in the region of £34 million. This estimate is based on the latest available cost (£34,000) of providing a psychiatric bed, together with associated day hospital places, in a new purpose-built general hospital unit. While the total figure of £34 million may appear daunting, the cost of an individual 50 bed unit would be about £1.7 million. This amount would represent a relatively small proportion of the overall cost of the major capital development schemes at present in progress or being planned in a number of general hospitals.

In-patient Service, New Long-stay Patients

15.5   The planning norm for accommodation for new long-stay psychiatric patients is 0.5 beds per 1,000 population. This consists of 0.4 beds in high support units and 0.1 beds in separate small nursing units for elderly persons who are demented and disturbed.

15.6   The planning guideline of 0.5 beds per 1,000 total population means that some 1,700 places are required nationally. It is not possible at this stage to give a precise indication of the capital resources which would be required to develop these facilities, as much will depend on local circumstances and on the type of accommodation used. Some options include the

—construction of purpose-built units

—purchase and adaptation of existing buildings

—use of existing health board properties

—leasing of suitable premises.

On the basis of present building costs, the construction of purpose-built units could cost £12,000 — £15,000 per place. If all the places needed were to be provided in purpose-built units, the maximum capital required would be in the region of £25 million. This sum would be required if existing health properties could not be used or if renting or leasing suitable properties was not an option. In practice, because of the potential for leasing and adapting existing premises, the actual expenditure required would probably be less than half this figure.

Day Facilities

15.7   In paragraph 6.15, we suggest that a target of 0.75 day places per 1,000 population served should be the immediate aim for local services. On a national basis this would involve a total of 2,600 places. At present there are some 1,180 places available throughout the country in a variety of day hospitals and day centres. The capital investment involved in the provision of the shortfall of 1,420 day places is difficult to estimate because these facilities, like many already available, can be partly provided by renting properties or by adapting existing health board premises. If new purpose-built accommodation was necessary in all cases, the maximum capital investment required would be in the region of £8 million based on the estimate of £5,500 per place for such accommodation. The actual sum required for extra accommodation should be much less. A figure of this order, however, would also enable a certain amount of existing day facilities, which are in substandard accommodation, to be improved or replaced by better buildings.

Community-Based Residences

15.8   In Chapter 9 we have set out policy guidelines on the development of community-based residences. There are some 950 places available in various types of hostels throughout the country at present. It is difficult to state precisely the total number of additional places which will be required nationally. The initial requirements will vary from one area to another and will depend on the backlog of existing long-stay patients. In addition, the number of domestic residences required will be affected by the success rate in placing patients in flats or lodgings. As set out in Chapter 9, we consider that health boards should give preference to renting suitable accommodation and, with the increased involvement of local housing authorities, the capital requirements should be limited. Where such resources are required, health boards may be able to use monies from their European Social Fund allocations for this purpose.

Minor Capital Improvement Schemes

15.9   In paragraph 10 of the Summary of Main Findings we referred to the valuable work undertaken in recent years with the special minor capital allocations for improvement works which have been approved for each district mental hospital. Between 1982 and 1984 a total of £6 million was allocated by the Department of Health for these schemes which have, amongst other things, facilitated the development of special rehabilitation units and hostel training facilities in many hospitals. The allocation of a similar amount in the period 1985 to 1987 will facilitate further progress and ensure an improved standard of accommodation for those long-stay patients who will spend the rest of their lives in psychiatric hospitals.

Total Capital Requirement

15.10   The total capital required to implement the recommendations of this Report could be in the region of £50 million, spent over a period of 10 to 15 years. While this is a substantial level of expenditure, we consider that there are compelling reasons why it should be committed. If the psychiatric service is not developed along the lines indicated in this Report, then the psychiatric hospitals will continue to accommodate a large number of patients. Most of these hospitals date from the middle of the last century and are now approaching the end of their lifespan. If they are to provide tolerable living accommodation for patients, an extensive programme to restructure and replace the existing stock of buildings must be undertaken. This would require a much larger investment of capital funds than would be involved in implementing the recommendations of this Report. If the existing hospital buildings were to be brought up to acceptable modern standards, or to be replaced where necessary with purpose-built in-patient units, the capital required could be in the region of £150 million.

15.11   Apart from the question of cost, we consider that investing on such a scale in psychiatric hospitals would be a disastrous path for this country to follow. It would perpetuate a pattern of care and treatment which is increasingly irrelevant to the real needs of the majority of the mentally ill in our society. It would, furthermore, be contrary to the main thrust of present psychiatric policy in other developed countries where the decentralisation of services and the move away from large psychiatric hospitals is continuing to gain momentum. We are firmly of the view that the money required to enable our recommendations to be implemented should be made available. We would emphasise that, while the main source of capital funding will continue to be allocation by the Department of Health to the health boards, other sources of capital funding, such as the sale of surplus psychiatric hospital land and the European Social Fund are also available and should be fully utilised.

Revenue Resources Required

15.12   The capital investment which we recommend over the coming years for the psychiatric service will not, in general, involve any additional revenue expenditure over and above the £145 million of revenue expenditure being

K

spent on the psychiatric service for 1984. The implementation of our recommendations will involve the development of new community psychiatric facilities, including the provision of high support hostels for new long-stay patients. In addition, the potential of the community care services, general practitioners and families to cope with persons with mental illness will be improved by increased liaison with the psychiatric service. This building up of services in the community will allow much of the specialised psychiatric service to be transferred from the hospitals, while the availability of residential accommodation in the community will allow many old long-stay patients to be discharged. In view of the age distribution of old long-stay patients, the numbers remaining in hospital can be expected to decline steadily as a result of death.

15.13   As in-patient numbers decline, there will be considerable potential for redeploying both staff and revenue resources from the hospitals to the new community services. This will be achieved by progressively closing down wards and sections of hospitals. There will be no need to increase the overall number of staff employed. However, as the service develops alone the lines we recommend, it will be necessary to convert a number of existing posts, at present based solely in the hospitals, into posts for specialised medical and paramedical staff, including posts in child psychiatry.

15.14   The redeployment of resources from the hospital has already started and new day services and other community facilities are being developed without incurring any additional revenue expenditure. We feel that this transfer of revenue resources will be the main challenge facing health boards and hospital managements over the coming years.

15.15   **Recommendations**

1. **There are compelling reasons why the money required to implement our recommendations should be made available (para. 15.10 and 15.11).**

2. **There should be a redeployment of revenue and staff resources from the hospitals to the new community services over the coming years (para. 15.13).**

3. **There should be a gradual conversion of a number of existing posts, based solely in the hospitals, into posts for specialised medical and paramedical staff, including posts in child psychiatry (para. 15.13).**

Chapter 16

Planning and Evaluation

16.1 The controlled implementation of the recommendations outlined in this Report requires that each health board draws up a realistic plan which will determine how the various parts of the service will inter-relate and the timescale for action. Local circumstances will determine much of the content of the plans and what is set out here are broad guidelines for planning. A number of stages may be identified in the planning process:

—identify the policy and objectives of the service;

—assemble the relevant information;

—draw up a plan of action for the specified time scale;

—implement the components of the plan in appropriate sequence;

—monitor progress in drawing up and implementing the plans;

—evaluate the benefits being achieved.

Policy Objectives

16.2 All actions designed to influence the health of the population rest on implicit or explicit policy objectives. The basic policy objectives of the psychiatric service might be regarded as the prevention of mental illness and, where this fails, the reduction as far as possible of impairments and disabilities which may result from illness.

16.3 Health strategy is the means by which these policy objectives are translated into action. In the case of the psychiatric service, the national strategy would be to move the care of the mentally ill away from large institutions to smaller, more manageable units in the community. The evidence available to us suggests that this is the most important single step which could be taken towards improving the delivery of mental health care.

Assemble Relevant Information

16.4   Good information is a necessary first step towards effective planning. The information required for planning the psychiatric service includes data on patients receiving services and on available services and their utilisation. We have substantial knowledge of the numbers and characteristics of patients in the various treatment facilities in this country and summaries of this information are contained in Appendix 3. It is essential, however, that each health board and each hospital should look carefully at its own patients to ascertain the degree of their impairments, the potential for rehabilitation and the type of facility needed for their rehabilitation. Guidelines for a survey of hospital patients are set out in paragraph 7.20. The survey should also include information on the staff and the buildings of each psychiatric hospital.

16.5   Information such as this, carefully collected and analysed, will make it possible to determine which patients are:

—primarily mentally handicapped,

—primarily geriatric,

—potentially suitable for discharge to community residence,

—actively disturbed patients with a low probability of being able to live in the community.

This information can be used to draw up programmes of rehabilitation and training and to provide guidance on the number of community residential places required. It will enable estimates to be made of the number of patients who will reside in the hospital at different points in the future. When this survey has been completed, arrangements should be made to collect a similar set of information on a regular basis for monitoring and planning purposes. The survey on hospital buildings, together with the information on patients, will allow plans to be made for structural improvements to selected parts of the buildings.

Draw up a Plan of Action

16.6   The compilation of good information on patients and resources will make it possible to design local plans of action. These plans should specify objectives which are realistic to the relevant sector, catchment area, or health board. They should also indicate the time scale within which the objectives should be reached. The following is a broad outline of what we consider should be the main features of a health board's plan:

1. divide the health board area into sectors;

2. assign responsibility for the psychiatric needs of each sector to a multidisciplinary team;

3. categorise patients in the psychiatric hospital or hospitals according to their varying needs and indicate how the hospital buildings will be used to accommodate them;

4. provide for programmes of training and rehabilitation both for patients who are resident in hospital and for those living in the community;

5. indicate the numbers and location of domestic scale residences required and the steps being taken to acquire them;

6. provide for a full range of community psychiatric services such as out-patient clinics, day care facilities, and supervised hostels, stating location and size together with the steps required to bring them into operation;

7. analyse different options for the location of the hospital in-patient service for short-stay and medium-stay patients;

8. specify the arrangements required to prevent inappropriate admissions to hospital and to ensure that patients are not admitted to long-stay wards;

9. include provision for high support hostels for new long-stay patients, indicating location, size and staffing;

10. indicate the means of establishing and strengthening links between the psychiatric and the community care services;

11. indicate, in broad outline, the steps to be taken to establish procedures for mental health consultation and for family support services;

12. indicate the expected shortages and surpluses in the different grades of staff as the psychiatric service evolves;

13. provide for programmes to retrain psychiatric nurses for their new role in:

    —rehabilitating and training patients to live in community settings, and

    —providing a community-based service.

16.7   Careful consideration should be given to the sequence of events in the plan. Some actions can take place immediately; others may depend on prior action on a related issue. For example, it will not be possible to discharge many patients to community residences until they have first completed a programme of training.

Implement the Plan

16.8   As soon as the outline of what is to be done is clear, there should be no delay in putting the plan of action into effect. Many components of the plan can be put into operation immediately and at little or no extra cost. For example, sectors can be designated by each health board and responsibility assigned to selected teams; programmes of patient training and rehabilitation can be put into operation; a number of community services can be established in existing facilities.

16.9   In formulating and implementing the plan, special attention must be given to the future role of the psychiatric hospitals and to the patients and staff of these hospitals. They must become active places, providing programmes of training and rehabilitation, to meet the varying needs of resident patients. All staff in the hospitals must be closely involved in achieving the ultimate objective of the hospital, which is to restore patients to as normal a life as possible in their own communities. An approach along these lines will ensure that the decline in the number of patients living in the hospitals will continue. Overcrowding has already been greatly reduced and should soon be eliminated. This will be followed by the closure of wards and a reduction in the number of beds available in the hospitals. This chain of events, together with the establishment of community facilities as outlined in this Report, must result in a transfer of activity from the hospitals to a variety of community-based facilities.

Monitor Progress

16.10   The process of planning is of little value unless it contains provision for ensuring that the plans are implemented and kept up to date. Planning must be a continuous process with changes being made in the light of new information as appropriate. There should be organisational arrangements which will ensure that:

—realistic plans are drawn up;

—the plans are implemented in a rational way and without unnecessary delay;

—there is continuing review of the plans and their implementation, with adjustments as need arises.

16.11   Each health board has primary responsibility for planning the service in its area, subject to overall guidance from the Department of Health. We do not propose any change in this division of responsibility but we do consider

134

that arrangements should be made to ensure that plans are drawn up and implemented. In this context, the Department of Health might consider setting up an advisory body which would consist of field workers in psychiatry, psychiatric nursing, psychiatric social work, clinical psychology and health administration. This body could have the role of assisting the Department in monitoring:

—the current state of the psychiatric service in each area;

—the formulation of plans for the future of the service and the revision of these plans as required;

—the implementation of these plans.

It could provide encouragement, guidance and assistance to the sector teams and to health board officials in designing and bringing about the required changes in the service.

Evaluate Benefits

16.12   Evaluation is an essential part of any health board or national plan. The process of evaluation should examine what has been achieved locally and nationally by the use of agreed indicators and by a comparison of indicators both within regions and between regions. Such indicators would include the number of occupied beds, the rate of decrease of occupied beds, the number of admissions and contacts with specialist psychiatric care, and the number of day places and hostel places. Evaluation should also focus on the quality of patient care provided.

16.13   To enable appropriate evaluation to take place, each health board or hospital will need to assemble and study more data than are currently being provided. These data will include information on in-patients and out-patients and a variety of other information concerning the operation of the psychiatric service. In parallel, budgetary and accounting information relating to costs of items of services provided for each patient need to be collected and studied. Finally, experimental studies of a cost-benefit or cost-effective nature, comparing the costs and benefits of alternative methods of treatment and rehabilitation, need to be undertaken.

16.14   We consider that the process of evaluation should include a self-evaluative check-list drawn up for the services in each sector. The items on the check-list could be based on the recommendations in this Report and should relate to the particular circumstances of the sector. It would be invaluable if an annual report was produced for each sector or catchment area, indicating the services provided and the progress being made in drawing up and implementing the plans. Evaluation on a national basis should be carried out by the Department of Health.

Staff Involvement

16.15   To the maximum extent possible, the staff providing the service should be involved in planning the future service for their locality. This might be done by way of formally established staff committees or more informally. The participation of staff in the early stages of planning ensures that their knowledge and experience are taken into account and helps to overcome the reservations which are inevitably associated with change.

Research

16.16   In Ireland, the level of resources devoted to psychiatric research is very small. In the United States, on the other hand, there is a requirement to set aside at least 2% of the psychiatric service budget for research and development. From a purely clinical standpoint, it is essential to have current and local epidemiological information on the illnesses being treated as well as up-to-date information on service utilisation. We welcome the recent, comprehensive survey of the practice of electroplexy in the Republic of Ireland[1] which represents the sort of research we have in mind. The Medico-Social Research Board has done important work in gathering data on the psychiatric services on a national basis. In child and family psychiatry, however, the basic epidemiological information on the situation in this country is lacking. In Chapter 12 we have recommended that an academic department of child and family psychiatry be established in one of our medical schools. We would envisage that such a department would undertake research in the specialty. We recommend that there should be more funding for research in both adult and child psychiatry.

16.17   Because many of the components of the psychiatric service we recommend are innovative, there is scope for many research projects to improve the current state of knowledge about their impact. For example, it will be necessary to evaluate the quality of care provided for patients at the different types of day care facilities and the need for separate day centres and day hospitals. In the course of this Report we have identified various gaps in information as well as the need for continuing research to provide more definite guidance on norms for service provision. We recommend that a number of studies should be carried out, as follows:

1. review of the norms recommended for day care services, in-patient services and community residential facilities;

136

2. study based on a sample of general practitioners to determine the number of patients they treat for mental illness;

3. effectiveness of general hospital psychiatric units;

4. feasibility of lodgings to house psychiatric patients;

5. prevalence by diagnostic category of mental infirmity in elderly people;

6. need for a specialised psychogeriatric service in different demographic circumstances.

16.18   A good information system will be essential to carry out the necessary research work. We recommend that steps be taken by the Department of Health to introduce a standard record for each patient which would be suitable for computer processing. In this regard the following recommendation which was contained in the World Health Organisation report "Changing Patterns in Mental Health Care"[2] is relevant:

> "A single type of documentation should be developed in each area, with careful regard for the confidentiality of personal data, so as to permit monitoring of the activities and utilisation of different parts of the service and reliable computing of basic statistics on patient care in all parts of the system e.g., for in-patients, day patients, out-patients, prevention, rehabilitation and after care".

16.19   There is also a need for a standardised patient record in child and family psychiatry. As well as providing a basis for a good information system, such standardisation will enable international comparisons and application of research findings to be made. Some of our child and family psychiatric services are already using a multi-axial classification scheme[3] based at present on the ninth edition of the World Health Organisation International Classification of Diseases. We recommend that this scheme, which is used internationally, should become the standard for all centres in Ireland.

16.20   **Recommendations**

1. **Plans should be drawn up by each health board to implement the recommendations of this Report (para. 16.1).**

2. **A survey of patients, staff and the buildings should be carried out in every psychiatric hospital (para. 16.4).**

3. **Health board plans of action should follow the guidelines set out in para. 16.6 of this Report.**

4. **The implementation of the plan should begin without delay. Particular attention should be given to the future role of the**

psychiatric hospitals and to the patients and staff of these hospitals (para. 16.8 and 16.9).

5. Each health board should have monitoring arrangments to ensure that plans are drawn up and implemented effectively (para. 16.10).

6. The Department of Health should consider setting up an advisory body to assist the Department in monitoring the changes occurring in the psychiatric service (para. 16.11).

7. Each health board should evaluate the benefits being achieved by the implementation of the plan in its area (para. 16.12).

8. As part of the process of evaluation, a check list should be drawn up for each sector based on the recommendations in this Report (para. 16.14).

9. As far as possible, staff should be involved in planning the future service for their locality (parà. 16.15).

10. There should be more funding for research in both child and adult psychiatry (para. 16.16).

11. A number of research projects should be carried out as outlined in para. 16.17.

12. A standard record for each patient which would be suitable for computer processing should be introduced by the Department of Health (para. 16.18).

13. A multi-axial classification scheme should become the standard for patient records in child and family psychiatry (para. 16.19).

Signed:

Shaun Trant, Chairman

Fergus Campbell

Anthony G. Carroll

Bob Daly

Donal Devitt

Martin Hynes

Peter McQuillan

Jim O'Boyle

Ronnie O'Sullivan

John Owens

Dermot Walsh

Frances Spillane, Secretary

Appendices

Appendix 1

The Epidemiology of Mental Illness

1.1   Various methods have been tried over the years to build up a picture of the extent of mental illness in a community. The main sources of this information which have emerged are:

—Hospital Data

—Psychiatric Case Registers

—Key Informant Surveys

—Community Surveys.

Hospital Data

Particulars will be given firstly about the resident patient population, secondly about admissions to hospital.

Resident Population

1.2   Despite the shift from residential treatment to community care which has been taking place since the report of the Commission of Inquiry on Mental Illness in 1966, our psychiatric hospital population remains notably higher than in most other countries. For example, in March 1981 the number of patients resident in Irish psychiatric hospitals and units, expressed as a rate per 100,000 population, was 406. The most up-to-date information available indicates corresponding rates for the following countries as follows:

England —   176[1]
France   —   228[2]
Denmark—   166[3]

1.3   Table 1 shows how the Irish hospitalisation rates compare with those of England by age.

143

TABLE 1

Number of patients resident in psychiatric hospitals and units in 1981, expressed as rates per 100,000 population for Ireland and for England, with ratio of rates

Age Group	Ireland	England	Ratio of Ireland to England
Under 15	7.4	5	1.5
15-19	46.0	22	2.1
20-24	142.7	49	2.9
25-34	275.2	88	3.1
35-44	517.3	94	5.5
45-54	792.4	144	5.5
55-64	1,036.8	240	4.3
65-74	1,229.3	382	3.2
75 and over	1,608.6	832	1.9

Note: The Irish rates are from the Irish Psychiatric Hospital Census 1981.[4] The English rates are estimates which have been supplied by the Department of Health and Social Security.

It is clear from this table that the Irish hospitalisation rates are greatly in excess of those in England.

1.4   The most relevant comment of the Commission of Inquiry on Mental Illness1966 on this state of affairs is worth quoting here:

"Statistics in respect of different countries may not be directly comparable, but, even if allowance is made for this, the number of in-patients in Ireland seems to be extremely high — it appears to be the highest in the world. It is hard to explain this. There are indications that mental illness may be more prevalent in Ireland than in other countries; however, there are many factors involved, and in the absence of more detailed research, the evidence to this effect cannot be said to be conclusive. Special demographic features, such as the high emigration rate, the low marriage rate and problems of employment, may be relevant to the unusually high rate of hospitalisation. In a largely rural country with few large centres of population, social and geographic isolation may affect both the mental health of individuals and the effectiveness of the mental health services. The public attitude towards mental illness may not be helpful to the discharge of patients and their reintegration in the community".

1.5   The major developments in drug treatment in the 1950s enabled doctors to treat the disturbed behaviour of psychiatric patients, so admission for long-term in-patient care became less necessary. These and other developments are reflected in the decline in the number of in-patients in public psychiatric hospitals in the 1960s and 1970s. In 1960 this number stood at 19,442; by 1970 it had fallen to 15,392 and in 1980 it was 12,212. The last detailed census of patients in Irish psychiatric hospitals and units was carried out in 1981 by the Medico-Social Research Board (M.S.R.B.).[4] Table 2 gives a percentage distribution of these patients by age and by length of stay.

TABLE 2

Percentage distribution of patients resident in psychiatric hospitals and units in 1981 by age and by length of stay

Age \ Length of stay	Less than 1 year	1-5 years	More than 5 years	All lengths of stay
Under 25	2.3	0.9	1.1	4.3
25-44	8.3	3.6	9.7	21.6
45-64	8.3	5.7	24.8	38.8
65 or over	6.0	7.0	22.2	35.2
All Ages	24.9	17.2	57.8	99.9

Hospital patients are often divided into two categories according to their length of stay in hospital. On the one hand there is the group comprising short-stay patients (i.e. those in hospital for less than one year) and, on the other hand, the balance who constitute the long-stay group. Table 2 shows that 75% of the resident population is in the long-stay category and that most of the patients in this category have been in hospital for more than 5 years. Furthermore the long-stay population tends to be older than the short-stay population; 39% of the long-stay patients were aged 65 or over; the corresponding proportion for the short-stay group was 24%.

Admissions

1.6   The other type of information that is available in relation to hospital statistics is that which relates to individual admissions and discharges. Here the trend is one of increasing activity. Table 3 illustrates this trend.

TABLE 3

Admissions to psychiatric hospitals and units — 1969 to 1982

Year	Number of Admissions	Percent First Admissions
1969	19,697	38.6
1970	20,343	37.7
1971	21,351	37.7
1972	22,964	37.4
1973	24,036	37.5
1974	24,964	35.7
1975	25,892	34.3
1976	26,434	33.8
1977	26,385	33.3
1978	27,662	31.4
1979	27,358	31.5
1980	27,098	31.2
1981	28,685	29.6
1982	28,778	30.2

L

There are also some psychiatric patients who are treated in general wards of general hospitals. On the basis of returns made to the Department of Health and to the Medico-Social Research Board under the Hospital In-Patient Enquiry Scheme, it has been estimated that the number of admissions involved could be of the order of 7,000 in a year. Accordingly, the total number of admissions to hospital for psychiatric conditions in 1982 was probably in the region of 35,000.

1.7 The set of patients admitted to hospital for the first time in any year is a subset of the total admissions for that year. Table 4 presents fairly clear evidence that Irish first admission rates[5] are considerably in excess of those for England.

TABLE 4
Ireland and England. First Admissions 1981.
Rates per 100,000 population with ratios of rates

Age Group	Male			Female		
	Ireland	England	Ratio of Ireland to England	Ireland	England	Ratio of Ireland to England
Under 15	9	15	0.6	6	12	0.5
15-19	144	66	2.2	113	86	1.3
20-24	373	118	3.2	241	126	1.9
25-34	484	120	4.0	334	143	2.3
35-44	562	115	4.9	391	131	3.0
45-54	453	95	4.8	345	119	2.9
55-64	379	93	4.1	343	122	2.8
65-74	365	139	2.6	351	171	2.1
75 and over	512	352	1.5	392	384	1.0
All age-groups	284	97	2.9	219	127	1.7

The trend in first admissions to Irish psychiatric hospitals and units from 1969 to 1982 is given in Table 5.

TABLE 5
First Admissions to psychiatric hospitals and units 1969 to 1982

Year	No. of First Admissions
1969	7,597
1970	7,673
1971	8,058
1972	8,598
1973	9,018
1974	8,914
1975	8,873
1976	8,939
1977	8,788
1978	8,678
1979	8,631
1980	8,459
1981	8,480
1982	8,702

No statistics are available on the extent to which first admissions occur in general hospitals.

Characteristics of patients admitted

1.8 *Sex.* In 1982 male admissions to psychiatric hospitals represented 55% of the total while in 1969 it was 52.4%. In every year since 1969 male admissions exceeded female admissions. The same pattern of male predominance emerged for first admissions, with males accounting for 55.6% in 1982 compared to 53% in 1969. One explanation for this phenomenon is the higher incidence of alcohol-related problems among males.

1.9 *Marital Status.* Table 6 gives a breakdown of the admissions to psychiatric hospitals in 1982, by marital status and sex.

TABLE 6

Admissions to psychiatric hospitals and units 1982 classified by marital status and sex

Marital Status	Male	Female	Total	Total rate per 100,000 population
Single	8,827	4,919	13,746	707.4
Married	5,633	6,068	11,701	938.6
Widowed	524	1,774	2,298	1,287.5
Unspecified	688	345	1,033	—
Total	15,672	13,106	28,778	854.3

Almost twice as many single men as single women were admitted but there was very little difference between the number of married men and married women. Rates per 100,000 relevant population were substantially greater for the widowed than for either the married or the single.

1.10 *Age on admission.* The greatest number of admissions to psychiatric hospitals and units in 1982 occurred between ages 25 and 34. The highest admission rate for males was in the age group 35 to 44 whereas the highest rate for females was in the 55 to 64 age group.

1.11 *Socio-economic groups.* The highest admission rates to psychiatric hospitals have been consistently recorded over the years by the "unskilled manual", "other agricultural" and the "non-manual" groups. If occupation is taken as a proxy for social class it is clear and that there is an inverse relationship between social class and psychiatric illness, that is the lower the social class the higher the rate of admission.

1.12 *Diagnosis.* In recent years depressive disorders have emerged as a major cause of admission to psychiatric hospitals. In 1982 this condition accounted for 26.5% of all admissions. Alcohol abuse and alcoholic psychosis accounted for the next largest category at 25.0%, and schizophrenia was the third largest, contributing 22.9%.

Case Registers

1.13   In considering the question of the extent of mental illness in the Irish community it is necessary to enquire beyond the level of the hospital. It could be, for instance, that the in-patient component in our psychiatric service is bigger than it is in other countries but that our total level of morbidity might not be all that excessive. The "case register" method is designed to record the numbers and characteristics of persons from defined catchment areas who come to any form of psychiatric treatment such as in-patient, hostel or out-patient care. A register is simply a list of the people concerned and of their relevant characteristics. A good example of this approach is the Three County Register set up in 1973 by the Medico-Social Research Board — one for each of counties Carlow, Westmeath and Roscommon. These counties were chosen because they best represented the spectrum of psychiatric morbidity and socio-demographic characteristics in Ireland.

1.14   The fairly detailed data required for the register are gathered by trained interviewers who use agreed standardised terms. The first step in building up the registers was to take a census of all the patients who were in psychiatric care in each county on 31 March 1973. After this date, as patients came into care they were added to the register and information up-dated as former patients returned to care. In addition, the registers contain information about persons from these counties who get their treatment from private psychiatric hospitals outside the three areas. In this way a broad picture is built up of all psychiatric illness that comes to the specialised psychiatric services from these three counties.

1.15   In Table 7 the one year prevalence rate for the three counties combined in 1981 is compared with those of the English registers in Southhampton, Nottingham, Oxford and Aberdeen in 1982. It may be seen from this table that the one year prevalence rate for the three counties combined in 1981 was greater than those of the English registers.

TABLE 7

One-year prevalence. Register rates per 100,000 population aged 15 or over.

Register	Register rate per 100,000 population
Three Counties (1981)	2295
Southhampton (1982)	2037
Nottingham (1982)	1905
Oxford (1982)	1644
Aberdeen (1982)	1986

148

1.16   Table 8 gives the rates for "one-day prevalence" for persons on the registers on 31 December 1982. These rates are calculated by relating the number of persons in psychiatric care to the population being served. For in-patients the relevant number of patients is the number in hospital at midnight on 31 March 1982 including patients 'on the books' or absent on leave. For out-patients the definition of being 'in care' on the census day is that of having made a contact with the psychiatric services at any time during the 90 days preceding census day.

TABLE 8

One day prevalence 1982 Register rates per 100,000 population aged 15 or over (1981 Census of population).

County	Register Rate per 100,000 population
Carlow	1989
Westmeath	1655
Roscommon	1706

An analysis of one-day prevalence data for the Three County Case Register on 31 December 1982 is contained in paragraphs 1.17 to 1.23.

1.17   *Age and Sex.*   Table 9 presents the Three County data in the form of rates per 100,000 population (1981 Census) aged 15 or over by age and sex. In general the rates increase with age.

TABLE 9

Number of persons in the Three Counties who were in care on 31/12/82 expressed as rates per 100,000 population aged 15 or over — by age and sex.

Age \ Sex	Male		Female		Total	
	Nos	Rates	Nos	Rates	Nos	Rates
15-19	10	128	10	137	20	132
20-24	41	646	27	475	68	565
25-34	126	1131	90	892	216	1018
35-44	145	1704	130	1678	275	1692
45-54	207	2664	173	2404	380	2539
55-64	223	2858	240	3232	463	3041
65+	302	3157	321	3152	623	3155
Total 15+	1054	1788	991	1782	2045	1785

1.18   *Diagnosis.*   Table 10 sets out the age-specific rates for the three counties combined for the principal diagnostic categories. In general the rates for schizophrenia and depressive disorders tend to increase with age and, as expected, the rates for organic psychoses are higher in the elderly.

TABLE 10

Number of persons in care on 31/12/82 expressed as rates per 100,000 population aged 15 or over — by age and diagnosis.

Diagnosis	15-24	25-44	45-64	65+	Total
Organic Psychosis	18	45	66	375	101
Schizophrenia	88	539	1103	1271	707
Depressive Disorder	44	163	480	613	296
Mania	7	53	242	268	129
Neurotic/Personality Disorder	70	200	374	278	229
Mental Handicap	66	219	278	172	190
Other Diagnoses	29	91	248	177	133
All Diagnoses	322	1310	2791	3154	1785

1.19 *Length of Stay.* Table 11 shows the age and length of stay data. The highest rates are in the long-stay category.

TABLE 11

Number of persons in care on 31/12/82 expressed as rates per 100,000 population aged 15 or over — by age and length of stay.

Age	Under 1 month	1-6 months	6 months-1 year	1 year or over	Total
15-19	20	40	13	60	133
20-24	42	141	108	274	565
25-34	57	188	137	636	1018
35-44	86	246	178	1181	1691
45-54	107	381	214	1837	2539
55-64	118	387	223	2312	3040
65+	66	243	167	2679	3155
Total 15+	71	233	150	1331	1785

1.20 *Length of Stay and Diagnosis.* Table 12 shows the length of stay rates for the chief diagnostic groups.

TABLE 12

Number of persons in care on 31/12/82 expressed as rates per 100,000 population aged 15 or over — by length of stay and diagnosis.

Diagnosis	Under 1 month	1-6 months	6 months-1 year	1 year or over	Total
Organic Psychosis	6	8	10	78	102
Schizophrenia	15	72	48	572	707
Depressive Disorder	19	51	38	187	295
Mania	8	31	20	70	129
Neurotic/Personality Disorder	11	38	17	162	228
Mental Handicap	—	4	3	182	189
Other Diagnoses	11	27	14	80	132
All Diagnoses	70	231	150	1331	1782

Table 12 shows that the greatest contribution to long-stay care in the three counties is made by schizophrenia. The proportion of all patients in long-term care in the three counties is quite large. It appears that, once in the psychiatric network, many patients never leave or leave only after prolonged periods of care.

1.21 *Diagnosis and Type of Care.*   Table 13 presents the rates for the major diagnostic groups by type of care.

TABLE 13

Numbers in care on 31/12/82 expressed as rates per 100,000 population aged 15 or over — by diagnosis and type of care

Diagnosis	In-patient	Out-patient	Total
Organic Psychosis	74	27	101
Schizophrenia	401	305	706
Depressive Disorder	76	220	296
Mania	50	79	129
Neurotic/Personality Disorder	56	173	229
Mental Handicap	167	24	191
Other Diagnoses	63	70	133
All Diagnoses	887	898	1,785

The broad distinction in Table 13 is between hospital in-patients and those in other forms of care e.g. hostels, day centres etc. who have been classified as out-patients. The in-patient rate for organic psychosis is higher than the out-patient rate. The in-patient rate for schizophrenia is also somewhat higher than the out-patient rate while more patients with depressive disorders are in out-patient care. Table 13 suggests that it is possible to treat persons with severe mental illness on an out-patient basis. Patients with neurotic and personality disorder are commoner as out-patients.

1.22 *Length of Stay by Type of Care.*   Table 14 gives the rates by length of stay and by type of care.

TABLE 14

Numbers in care on 31/12/82 expressed as rates per 100,000 population aged 15 or over — by length of stay and type of care

Length of Stay	In-patient	Out-patient	Total
Under 1 Month	31	40	71
1-6 Months	51	182	233
6 Months-1 Year	24	126	150
1 Year and over	781	550	1,331
All Lengths of Stay	887	898	1,785

This table shows that the out-patient rate is higher than the in-patient rate for each length of stay category up to one year. Chronicity is noticeable and

151

this is, somewhat surprisingly, true of out-patient illness as well as in-patient. About 88% of in-patients and 61% of out-patients are long-stay.

1.23 *Socio-Economic Groups* The prevalence date from the Three County Register tend to confirm the position outlined in paragraph 1.11 in relation to the incidence of mental illness viz. the lower the socio-economic group the higher the rate of prevalence. This is clear from Table 15.

TABLE 15

Number of persons in care on 31/12/82 expressed as a rate per 100,000 population aged 14 or over in selected socio-economic groups

Socio-Economic Group	Rate
Higher Professional	472
Employers and Managers	538
Salaried Employees	707
Other non-manual	2,102
Other agricultural	2,756
Unskilled manual	3,633

1.24 The analysis in paragraph 1.17 to 1.23 highlights some important features of psychiatric illness in Ireland.
These are—

1. Most treated psychiatric illness is long-stay (para. 1.19).

2. About a third of patients in care are elderly (para. 1.17).
3. Most in-patients suffer from severe or psychotic forms of illness (para. 1.21).

4. Expansion of services outside of hospital attracts a newer group of persons suffering from less severe illnesses many of whom eventually become long-stay in out-patient care (para. 1.21-1.22).

5. Development of out-patient and other community services appears to provide alternative care for some patients with severe illnesses such as schizophrenia and manic depressives who otherwise would be dealt with exclusively by hospitalisation (para. 1.21).

Key Informant Surveys

1.25 One of the limitations of the case register approach is that it deals only with cases of psychiatric illness attending the specialised services. It does not include cases of psychiatric illness treated by general practitioners or illness that is undetected and not being treated at all in the community. One approach to tapping this source of illness is to use the "key informant" method whereby those people in the community who are likely to know, such as general practitioners, public health nurses, teachers, and gardaí are asked to report on anyone whom they think may be suffering from mental illness.

Community Surveys

1.26   Large-scale studies of community morbidity are the most comprehensive way of measuring the prevalence of psychiatric illness but these are beyond the resources of all but a minority of research groups. No such type of survey has ever been attempted in Ireland. However, small scale community surveys of severe psychiatric illness in Ireland have been carried out.[7, 8]

1.27   An example of a community survey is the work which has been carried out by Bebbington and his co-workers concerning psychiatric disorders among the population aged 18-64 of Camberwell in London.[9] The survey consisted of two stages. A random sample of names was drawn from the relevant electoral register. In the first stage 800 interviews were carried out by trained interviewers who administered the short form (40 items) of a psychiatric questionnaire called the Present State Examination (PSE). By analysing the PSE data from this first interview it was possible to establish a threshold level for psychiatric illness. The second stage consisted of a more detailed interview involving the full 140 item PSE and the group interviewed this time consisted of 310 persons including most of those who were determined on the basis of the first interview to be above the threshold i.e. "psychiatric cases". The prevalence of psychiatric disorder as defined in this study was 10.9% of the population aged 18-64 and this reflected rates of 6.1% for men and 14.9% for women.

1.28   Several other prevalence estimates derived from surveys carried out in the 1970s in Europe and the United States have worked out in the range 4-8% for men and 8-15% for women. Nearly all the surveys demonstrate a prevalence in women about twice that in men despite the wide differences in methods of case finding and sampling. These estimates tend to support the British National Morbidity Survey carried out in 1970-71 which showed that on average over the year, 7% of males and 14% of females consulted their general practitioners for some form of mental illness. Very recently what is probably the most extensive and comprehensive community survey on mental illness ever undertaken has been set up in the United States.[10] Preliminary results from this study are beginning to appear and suggest that when alcohol and drug abuse are taken into account there may be no difference between the sexes in prevalence rates for mental disorder.

Number of Mentally Ill Persons

1.29   The estimates in the preceding paragraph seem to suggest that the prevalence of mental illness could be of the order of 10% of the population aged 18 to 64. If this were to be applicable in Ireland it would be equivalent to about a fifth of a million people nationally (excluding children). For prevalence rates in children, see paragraph 12.9.

Appendix 2

Psychiatric Services for the Adult Deaf

(Prepared by Dr. Jim O'Boyle)

Introduction

2.1   During the last twenty-five years provision of specialised services for deaf adults has been a feature of the development of comprehensive psychiatric services in many countries, particularly in North America. In this country we have not, as yet, developed such a service. Deaf adults requiring psychiatric treatment are assessed and treated in a setting which is not equipped for those who are suffering from severe hearing impairment. The objective in setting up specialised psychiatric services for the deaf in other countries has been to provide assessment, diagnosis and treatment at a centre where all staff members are skilled in communicating with the deaf.

Definition of Deafness

2.2   Deafness is a term which includes all types of hearing impairment due to a defect in the hearing mechanism. The degree of deafness ranges from total loss of hearing for any kind of sound in any circumstance to a mild degree of deafness which may be almost imperceptible.[1] Prelingual deafness is present from birth, or occurs in the early years of life before the development of speech and language. Post-lingual deafness occurs after the acquisition of language. Post-lingual deafness occurs after the acquisition of language. The term prelingual profound deafness should be confined to hearing impairment which is profound and cannot be alleviated to any useful degree by hearing aids, and which is either congenital or acquired in early life before the development of speech and language.[2]

2.3   Severe hard of hearing is the term used for children who have had considerable speech experience, but are so handicapped by defective hearing that they require to be educated in small classes by a teacher of the deaf using modern electronic equipment.[1]

2.4   A deaf person is not necessarily mute. Speech proficiency is related to the age of onset of deafness in addition to the opportunities which the deaf person has received for special training and the acquisition of language.

154

Incidence of Deafness

2.5   There are no statistics available for the incidence of deafness in the adult population in this country. The incidence of profound deafness between 3 and 18 years of age is of the order of 4 to 4.5 per 10,000 of the school-going population. The incidence of severely hard of hearing children is estimated to be 5 per 10,000.[1] It is estimated by the National Association of the Deaf that the incidence of profound deafness is 1 per 1,000 of the general population.

Complications of Deafness

2.6   Social isolation is recognised as one of the principal complications of profound or severe hearing impairment.[3] The primary cause of social isolation in the deaf is the sensory defect which interferes with normal communication and social interaction.[4] The problem of social isolation is reinforced in the deaf patient if he is admitted to a large psychiatric hospital, because he cannot communicate through speech and lip-reading if he is not in a unit with other deaf patients with whom he might be able to communicate by using sign-language. The stress of this situation for the deaf patient is further increased by the lack of communication skills in the medical and nursing staff caring for him.[5] People generally have little difficulty in understanding and identifying with those who are blind, whereas deafness is a handicap which is much less readily understood because it is not visible.[7]

2.7   In a British study of 170 deaf adults, the majority of whom were profoundly deaf, attending a special psychiatric service for the deaf, the patients were divided into a number of diagnostic groups. The largest group consisted of 72 patients who were diagnosed as suffering from behaviour and maladjustment problems related to their deafness. They were not considered to be suffering from a formal psychiatric illness. Problems of maladjustment are recognised as being extremely common in the deaf.[3] A second group of 56 patients were diagnosed as suffering from mental illness which was coincidental with deafness. A diagnosis of schizophrenia was made in 36 of these patients. Many of the signs of psychiatric illness e.g. the thought disorder of schizophrenia, are appreciated through normal spoken language. Any communication difficulty will interfere with this appreciation.[6] A third group of 22 patients were diagnosed as suffering from what was termed a development disorder of communication, and of this group, 9 patients were suffering from deafness and mental handicap and a further 5 patients suffered from deafness and autism.

2.8   Research studies in the U.S.A. suggest that the prevalence of schizophrenia in the prelingually deaf is similar to that in the hearing population. There is, however, some evidence that paranoid schizophrenia may be more prevalent among the post-lingually deaf and the hard of hearing than in the general population.[5]

2.9   The characteristics of deafness which are likely to be significant in the causation of paranoid psychosis are:—

early age of onset

long duration

severity of deafness.

The mode of action of deafness in the genesis of paranoid psychosis is most likely to be one in which psychological function and social function change over an extended time-span of years.[4]

2.10   There is a high risk of mis-diagnosis in deaf adults suffering from psychiatric illness who are treated in a setting where the staff are not skilled in the use of sign-language. Abnormal behaviour arising from a psychotic illness may erroneously be ascribed to deafness or vice versa i.e. abnormal behaviour resulting from deafness may be considered to be due to a psychosis.[7]

2.11   A study[9] of six large psychiatric hospitals in this country, undertaken in 1983, by a teacher for the deaf skilled in sign-language, identified a total of 23 (15 male and 8 female) deaf adult in-patients. Each hospital was visited and each patient and the respective medical and nursing staff caring for the patients were also interviewed. Twenty-one of the patients were suffering from severe hearing impairment. The remaining two patients had never attended any special school for the deaf, but were considered to have needed special education, and as a consequence had not developed any expressive means of communication. The age range of the patients was as follows:—

Under age 30 — 4 patients

31-35 — 11 patients

Over 50 — 8 patients

Length of stay in hospital was as follows:—

Less than one year — 2 patients

Between 1-10 years — 4 patients

Period of 11-20 years — 9 patients

More than 21 years — 8 patients

One patient had spent thirty nine years in hospital.

2.12   It is significant that in discussion with the medical staff in the different hospitals, only seven of the 23 patients were considered by the medical staff to be suffering from a form of psychiatric illness. This did not include four patients who were diagnosed as suffering from mental handicap. There was only one patient given a definite diagnosis of schizophrenia. Twelve of the 23 patients had good sign-language skills and could also communicate adequately by writing. The remainder of the patients had varying degrees of skill in communication. None of the medical staff in the hospitals had any special skills in sign-language. This study suggests the need for a survey in our other psychiatric hospitals to establish the prevalence of severe deafness in the in-patient population, and the presence or absence of an associated formal psychiatric illness.

Support Services For the Adult Deaf

2.13   The principal voluntary organisation providing a support service for the deaf is the National Association for the Deaf (N.A.D.). A social worker who is employed by this association provides a service to the deaf and their families, but is also available on a national basis for the law courts if a communication problem should arise.

2.14   The National Rehabilitation Board employs a youth employment officer to work with school-leavers in special schools for the deaf, the majority of whom finish school aged 15 or 17 years, having completed either the Group or Leaving Certificate Examination. The function of the youth employment officer is to help in placing young deaf adults in suitable employment or in training courses/third level education on leaving school. In addition, each health board area has the services of a placement officer, who is employed by the National Rehabilitation Board, each of whom has a number of deaf adults who are his responsibility. There is also a special placement officer for the deaf, based in Dublin, who acts in an advisory capacity to the regional placement officers working with the health boards throughout the country. The Department of Education employs a special teacher for the deaf who acts as a liaison person and who helps to resolve difficulties between trainees and their supervisors/employers.

2.15   The only hostel accommodation which caters specifically for the adult deaf is at St Joseph's House for Adult Deaf/Deaf Blind, at Brewery Road, Stillorgan, Co Dublin. This hostel was founded in 1965 by the Catholic Committee for the Deaf and its principal objective was to cater for deaf geriatric adults who were living in isolated situations in the community. In recent years, a number of younger people have been admitted to St Joseph's and at present of the total of 37 residents, 17 have formerly been in-patients in psychiatric hospitals for varying lengths of time. The hostel is supervised by the Dominican Sisters from the Dominican Convent in Cabra, who specialise in the care of the deaf and the deaf blind. The staff includes: resident house-parents, one of whom is a trained teacher of the deaf, visiting medical officer, visiting speech therapist, occupational therapist and teacher of the deaf/blind. The majority of residents are profoundly deaf. One of the criteria for admission to this hostel is that the applicant should be free of any anti-social behaviour, because of the limited supervision available and the number of elderly residents.

Conclusions

1. There is a need for a survey to be undertaken of all psychiatric hospitals using researchers who are highly proficient in communication skills with the deaf to determine the prevalence of severe hearing impairment and the presence or absence of a formal psychiatric illness in the in-patient population. This survey would give an indication of the number of patients who have been inappropriately placed in our psychiatric hospitals in the absence of suitable alternatives.

2. A separate out-patient service should be available in each health board area to the adult deaf presenting for a psychiatric consultation. All staff working in this service should receive special training in sign-language.

3. There is a need for supervised hostels for the adult deaf. These would be set up on a pilot project basis, when the results of the in-patient deaf survey have been completed. In association with the establishment of such special hostels for the deaf, a supporting rehabilitation programme will be required so that residents may be trained for placement in open employment. An important member of any rehabilitation team will be a teacher for the deaf who will provide classes to improve the communication skills of both the deaf patients and the staff.

4. The staff in the out-patient special service for the deaf should be available to follow-up patients who may be admitted to a psychiatric unit for further assessment and treatment.

5. A social worker from every community care programme should be seconded for special training in sign-language with a view to having the social worker available to liaise between the deaf adults, their employers, and family.

6. Where a number of deaf patients are resident in a large psychiatric hospital, steps should be taken to ensure that these patients are, wherever possible, brought together in the same unit to reduce the risk of social isolation and to encourage interpersonal communication.

Appendix 3

Statistics on Psychiatric Services and Staffing

3.1 In this Appendix statistics are presented on:

(a) In-Patient Services

(b) Community Services

(c) Staffing.

(a) In-Patient Services

3.2 Three tables are presented on individual psychiatric hospitals and units. Table 1 deals with health board hospitals and units and shows the number of patients in residence at the end of 1981, 1982 and 1983 together with a break-down of the number of admissions during 1982 in 3 age-groups. Similar statistics in respect of private and special hospitals are given in Tables 2 and 3 respectively. Table 4 summarises Tables 1 to 3 and presents the national picture.

TABLE 1
Health board psychiatric hospitals and units: numbers of admissions during 1982 by age and number of in-patients at 31 December, 1981, 1982 and 1983

Health Board and Hospital	Number of Admissions during 1982				Number of patients in hospital at 31 December		
	Under 45 years	45-64 years	65 years and over	Total	1981	1982	1983
EASTERN							
St. Brendan's	830	469	265	1,564	953	947	932
St. Ita's	361	167	58	586	974	967	930
St. Loman's	840	353	83	1,276	169	172	163
St. Dympna's Alcoholic Unit	172	83	4	259	12	14	11
Unit at Vergemount, Clonskeagh	103	63	27	193	25	29	23
Unit at St. Vincent's, Fairview	326	196	105	627	N.A.	N.A.	N.A.
St. James's	138	121	61	320	45	50	49
Newcastle Hospital, Co. Wicklow	181	136	60	377	103	108	89
Cluain Mhuire	221	111	34	366	79	67	71
St. Patrick's (health board)	N.A.	N.A.	N.A.	N.A.	56	50	61
St. Vincent's, Elm Park	N.A.	N.A.	N.A.	N.A.	24	23	20
Total — Eastern	3,172	1,699	697	5,568	2,440	2,427	2,349

Health Board and Hospital	Number of Admissions during 1982				Number of patients in hospital at 31 December		
	Under 45 years	45-64 years	65 years and over	Total	1981	1982	1983
MIDLAND							
St. Fintan's, Portlaoise	380	251	105	736	406	396	405
St. Loman's, Mullingar	587	423	201	1,211	742	732	719
Total — Midland	967	674	306	1,947	1,148	1,128	1,124
MID-WESTERN							
Our Lady's, Ennis	296	229	102	627	626	609	567
Unit at Regional General Hospital, Limerick	288	194	78	560	23	32	28
St. Joseph's, Limerick	985	481	165	1,631	694	707	640
Total — Mid-Western	1,569	904	345	2,818	1,343	1,348	1,235
NORTH-EASTERN							
St. Brigid's, Ardee	232	141	94	467	235	209	192
St. Davnet's, Monaghan	333	360	152	845	416	389	378
Total — North-Eastern	565	501	246	1,312	651	598	570
NORTH-WESTERN							
St. Conal's, Letterkenny	478	350	179	1,007	502	502	470
Unit at General Hospital, Letterkenny[a]	—	—	—	—	N.A.	N.A.	N.A.
St. Columba's, Sligo	390	291	169	850	587	567	542
Total — North-Western	868	641	348	1,857	1,089	1,069	1,012
SOUTH-EASTERN							
St. Dympna's, Carlow	321	216	80	617	366	392	374
St. Canice's, Kilkenny	168	114	85	367	346	368	323
St. Luke's, Clonmel	315	182	118	615	476	491	450
Unit at St. Joseph's, Clonmel	385	301	185	871	37	43	43
St. Otteran's, Waterford	204	210	76	490	420	390	364
St. Declan's Unit, Ardkeen Hospital	183	140	103	426	29	23	35
St. Senan's, Enniscorthy	228	157	116	501	392	348	327
Total — South Eastern	1,804	1,320	763	3,887	2,066	2,058	1,916
SOUTHERN							
Our Lady's, Cork	547	285	138	970	1,005	1,004	918
Unit at St. Stephen's, Sarsfieldcourt	485	252	113	850	111	113	90
Unit at Regional Hospital, Wilton	408	238	113	759	44	40	52
St. Anne's, Skibbereen	166	145	99	410	12	17	16
St. Finan's, Killarney	355	283	153	791	603	597	605
Total — Southern	1,961	1,203	616	3,780	1,775	1,771	1,681

Health Board and Hospital	Number of Admissions during 1982				Number of patients in hospital at 31 December		
	Under 45 years	45-64 years	65 years and over	Total	1981	1982	1983
WESTERN							
St. Brigid's, Ballinasloe	450	311	126	887	1,030	993	952
St. Mary's, Castlebar	509	316	226	1,051	618	598	583
St. Theresa's Unit at Castlebar General Hospital[b]	N.A.	N.A.	N.A.	N.A.	37	41	43
Unit at Regional Hospital, Galway	291	149	97	537	39	37	38
St. Patrick's, Castlerea	158	163	125	446	264	259	238
Total — Western	1,408	939	574	2,921	1,988	1,928	1,854
TOTAL	12,314	7,881	3,895	24,090	12,500	12,327	11,741

N.A. = not available.

[a]The unit at the General Hospital Letterkenny is used partially by psychiatric patients and the number of patients there is included in those for St. Conals.

[b]The number of admissions for St. Theresa's Unit at Castlebar General Hospital is included with those for St. Mary's, Castlebar.

Source: Number of admissions — Medico-Social Research Board.

TABLE 2

Private psychiatric hospitals: number of admissions during 1982 by age and number of in-patients at 31 December, 1981, 1982 and 1983

Health Board and Hospital	Number of Admissions during 1982				Number of Patients in hospital at 31 December		
	Under 45 years	45-64 years	65 years and over	Total	1981	1982	1983
EASTERN							
Bloomfield, Donnybrook, Dublin	0	0	13	13	57	54	57
Hampstead, Highfield and Elmhurst	4	6	16	26	81	70	68
Kylemore Clinic, Co. Dublin	5	31	34	70	21	24	26
Palmerstown House, Co. Dublin	5	5	0	10	3	5	5
St. John of God, Dublin	663	578	171	1,412	105	117	107
St. Patrick's, James's St. and St. Edmondsbury, Lucan, Co. Dublin[a]	1,000	820	302	2,122	313	322	301
St. Vincent's, Fairview, Dublin[b]	31	31	7	69	160	136	109
Verville Retreat, Clontarf, Dublin	2	5	7	14	50	50	50
Total — Eastern	1,710	1,476	550	3,736	790	778	723
NORTH-EASTERN							
St. Augustine's, Ratoath Co. Meath	0	0	15	15	58	55	56
Total — North-Eastern	0	0	15	15	58	55	56

M

Health Board and Hospital	Number of admissions during 1982				Number of patients in hospital at 31 December		
	Under 45 years	45-64 years	65 years and over	Total	1981	1982	1983
SOUTH-EASTERN							
Bon Sauveur, Carriglea, Co. Waterford	0	0	0	0	2	2	2
St. Patrick's, Belmont Park, Waterford	361	148	50	559	75	71	79
Total — South-Eastern	361	148	50	559	77	73	81
SOUTHERN							
Lindville, Blackrock Road, Co. Cork	61	60	13	134	36	38	36
Total — Southern	61	60	13	134	36	38	36
TOTAL	2,132	1,684	628	4,444	961	944	896

[a]Number of admissions relate to St. Patrick's only. See Table 1 for health board patients resident in St. Patrick's.

[b]The number of patients in hospital refers to both private and health board patients in St. Vincent's Hospital, Fairview.

Source: Number of admissions — Medico-Social Research Board.

TABLE 3

Special psychiatric hospitals: number of admissions during 1982 by age and number of in-patients at 31 December, 1981, 1982 and 1983

Health Board and Hospital	Number of admissions during 1982				Number of patients in hospital at 31 December		
	Under 45 years	45-64 years	65 years and over	Total	1981	1982	1983
EASTERN							
Central Mental Hospital, Dundrum	162	4	0	166	94	95	96
St. Paul's, Beaumont	8	0	0	8	25	26	27
Warrenstown House, Blanchardstown Road	25	0	0	25	16	14	13
Total — Eastern	195	4	0	199	135	135	136
WESTERN							
St. Anne's, Galway	45	0	0	45	22	[a]22	29
Total — Western	45	0	0	45	22	22	29
TOTAL	240	4	0	244	157	157	165

Notes: The Central Mental Hospital, Dundrum is the national centre for offenders suffering from mental disorders. St. Paul's is a special hospital run by the Sisters of Mercy, Mater Hospital for autistic and emotionally disturbed children and patients are admitted in the same manner as to a general hospital. Warrenstown House, Dublin and St. Anne's, Galway are both centres for emotionally disturbed children run by the Eastern and Western Health Boards respectively.

[a] = Estimate.

Source: Number of admissions — Medico-Social Research Board.

TABLE 4

All psychiatric hospitals and units: number of admissions during 1982 by age and number of in-patients at 31 December 1981, 1982, and 1983 analysed by health board area

Health Board	Number of admissions during 1982				Number of patients in hospital at 31 December		
	Under 45 years	45-64 years	65 yrs and over	Total	1981	1982	1983
Eastern	5,077	3,179	1,247	9,503	3,365	3,340	3,208
Midland	967	674	306	1,947	1,148	1,128	1,124
Mid-Western	1,569	904	345	2,818	1,343	1,348	1,235
North-Eastern	565	501	261	1,327	709	653	626
North-Western	868	641	348	1,857	1,089	1,069	1,012
South-Eastern	2,165	1,468	813	4,446	2,143	2,131	1,997
Southern	2,022	1,263	629	3,914	1,811	1,809	1,717
Western	1,453	939	574	2,966	2,010	1,950	1,883
Total	14,686	9,569	4,523	28,778	13,618	13,428	12,802

Note: This table is a summary of the data contained in Tables 1, 2 and 3. The footnotes relevant to these tables still apply.

Source: Number of admissions—Medico-Social Research Board.

3.3 In Table 5, the number of patients resident in public psychiatric hospitals and units on 31st December, 1983 is summarised by age and length of stay.

TABLE 5

Number of patients resident in public psychiatric hospitals and units at 31 December 1983 by age and length of stay.

Length of stay \ Age	Under 15	15-19	20-44	45-64	65-74	75 and over	All ages	% of Hospital Population
Under 3 months	1	31	587	605	264	122	1,610	13.9
3-12 months	3	10	270	294	154	103	834	7.2
1-5 years	7	18	551	712	412	383	2,083	17.9
Over 5 years	5	11	1,221	3,030	1,674	1,145	7.086	61.0
All lengths of stay	16	70	2,629	4,641	2,504	1,753	11,613*	100.0
% of Hospital Population	0.1	0.6	22.6	40.0	21.6	15.1	100.0	

*The total of 11,613 patients excludes the Health Board patients at Cluain Mhuire Hospital, Dublin and St Patrick's Hospital, Dublin as this information was not available. Patients in special psychiatric hospitals (see Table 3) are also excluded.

Source: Department of Health.

3.4 The decline in the number of patients resident in public psychiatric hospitals and units between 1940 and 1983 is shown in Table 6.

TABLE 6

Number of in-patients in public psychiatric hospitals and units 1940-1983

Year	Number of In-Patients
1940	19,134
1945	17,708
1950	18,677
1955	19,810
1960	19,442
1965	17,594
1970	15,392
1975	13,869
1980	12,212
1983	11,741

Note: In-patients in special psychiatric hospitals are not included.

Source: Department of Health.

3.5 Censuses of patients in psychiatric hospitals and units were carried out in 1963, 1971 and 1981. Table 7 compares the main findings.

TABLE 7

Psychiatric patients in residence by sex, age, marital status, length of stay and diagnosis 1963, 1971 and 1981

	1981	1971	1963
Number of patients in residence at 31 March	13,984	16,661	19,801
Percentage who were: male	55.3	55.5	54.3
female	44.7	44.5	45.7
Percentage who were: aged under 25	4.3	5.9	5.0
aged 25-64	60.4	63.7	70.0
aged 65 or over	35.3	30.4	24.9
Percentage who were: single	79.5	82.2	82.1
married	13.0	11.8	12.6
widowed	6.5	5.8	5.3
Percentage who were: shortstay (less than 1 month)	10.5	7.7	N.A.
medium stay (1 month to 1 year)	14.4	15.1	N.A.
long stay (1 year or over)	75.1	77.2	N.A.

164

	1981	1971	1963
Percentage in each diagnostic category*			
Organic psychosis		10.9	13.8
Schizophrenia		50.1	53.0
Manic depressive psychosis		12.3	12.9
Other and unspecified psychoses		2.1	
Neurosis		3.3	4.9
Personality disorder		1.3	
Alcoholism and alcoholic psychosis		2.4	1.5
Drug addiction		0.1	
Mental handicap		16.1	13.8
Unspecified		1.4	0.1
*Percentage in each diagnostic category			
Organic psychosis	10.2		
Schizophrenia	44.2		
Other and unspecified psychosis	0.4		
Depressive disorders	11.1		
Mania	5.7		
Neurosis	5.7		
Personality disorder	2.1		
Alcohol abuse and alcoholic psychosis	4.9		
Drug dependence	0.1		
Mental handicap	15.5		
Unspecified	0.1		

Note: Some of the diagnostic categories were re-organised for the 1981 Census. The main changes concerned the affective disorders, neuroses and to a lesser extent alcoholism.

Source: Medico-Social Research Board.

3.6   Tables 8 and 9 analyse certain demographic characteristics and the diagnoses of persons admitted to psychiatric hospitals during 1982.

TABLE 8

Admissions to psychiatric hospitals and units, analysed by marital status, age and sex of patients, 1982

	Number	Per cent of all admissions
Total admissions	28,778	100.0
First-time admissions	8,702	30.2
Marital status of patients who were admitted:		
single	13,746	47.8
married	11,701	40.6
widowed	2,298	8.0
unspecified	1,033	3.6

	Number	Per cent of all admissions
Age of patients who were admitted:		
under 25 years	2,760	9.6
25-44 years	11,926	41.4
45-64 years	9,569	33.3
65 years and over	4,523	15.7
Sex of patients who were admitted:		
male	15,672	54.5
female	13,106	45.5

Source: Medico-Social Research Board

TABLE 9

Admissions to psychiatric hospitals and units: Rate per 100,000 population by diagnosis age and sex, 1982

Diagnosis	Sex		Age			
	Male	Female	20-24	35-44	65-74	Total
Organic Psychosis	34.6	38.1	10.8	18.8	169.7	36.6
Schizophrenia	225.2	165.4	224.2	425.5	157.1	195.5
Other and Unspecified Psychoses	2.8	4.4	3.3	7.6	7.6	3.6
Depressive Disorders	162.0	291.3	136.3	368.4	604.9	226.3
Mania	55.9	85.8	48.0	117.7	156.7	70.8
Neurosis	35.3	64.0	54.0	90.5	74.9	49.1
Personality Disorder	40.3	33.7	76.6	57.9	21.9	37.1
Alcohol Abuse and Alcoholic Psychosis	344.8	80.5	112.2	605.4	193.8	213.4
Drug Dependence	8.2	4.7	21.4	11.1	1.6	6.5
Mental Handicap	13.8	10.2	21.7	25.9	5.1	12.0
Unspecified	3.1	3.8	5.6	5.6	4.2	3.4
Total	925.5	782.4	714.6	1,735.4	1,398.6	854.3

Source: Medico-Social Research Board.

(b) Community Services

Day Facilities

3.7 Table 10 compares the number of day facilities for the mentally ill in each health board area in 1981, 1982 and 1983. Table 11 lists the location of these facilities and the number of places in each.

166

TABLE 10

Day facilities: Comparison of number of day facilities for the mentally ill in 1981, 1982, 1983.

Health Board	Number of Day Facilities		
	1981	1982	1983
Eastern	15	19	20
Midland	—	—	—
Mid-Western	1	1	1
North-Eastern	4	3	4
North-Western	2	2	2
South-Eastern	1	1	1
Southern	3	3	3
Western	6	6	8
Total	32	35	39

Note: The North-Western Health Board also provides limited day care facilities for the mentally ill at 11 geriatric institutions throughout the NWHB area.

TABLE 11

Day Facilities: Location and number of places available in day facilities for the mentally ill 1983

Health Board and Location of Day Facility	Number of Places
EASTERN HEALTH BOARD (a)	
Dun Laoghaire and South East Dublin County	
Centenary House, 35 York Road, Dun Laoghaire, Co. Dublin (St. John of God)	30
Burton Hall, Foxrock, Co. Dublin (St. John of God)	30
Cluain Mhuire Day Hospital, Blackrock, Co. Dublin (St. John of God)	50
Dublin South-East	
Vergemount Day Centre, Clonskeagh, Dublin 6	42
Day Care Centre, 31 Mountpleasant Square, Ranelagh, Dublin 6	40
Dublin South Central	
Day Hospital, Hospital 6, St. James' Hospital, James' Street, Dublin 8 (St. Patrick's Hospital)	
St. Patrick's Day Centre, St. Patrick's Hospital, James' Street, Dublin 8 (St. Patrick's Hospital)	50
Usher's Island Day Centre, Dublin 8	50
	30
Dublin West and Kildare North	
St. Loman's Hospital Day Centre, Palmerstown, Dublin 20	60
Kilcock Day Centre, Co. Kildare	26
Dublin North West	
St. Brendan's Hospital Day Centre, Grangegorman, Dublin 7	80
Day Centre, 230 North Circular Road, Dublin 7	20
Finglas Training Centre, North Road, Dublin 11	40
Wellmount Park Day Centre, Finglas, Dublin 11	20
St. Dympna's Mews Day Care Centre, North Circular Road, Dublin 7 (Irish Society for Autistic Children)	10
St. Dympna's Day Hospital, North Circular Road, Dublin 7	55

Health Board and Location of Day Facility	Number of Places
Dublin North Central St. John's Day Centre, Clontarf, Dublin 3	75
Dublin North East St. Francis's Day Hospital, Raheny, Dublin 5 St. Ita's Hospital Day Centre, Portrane, Co. Dublin	30 20
Wicklow An Lar Day Centre, Dargle Road, Bray, Co. Wicklow	26
TOTAL EASTERN (a)	784
MIDLAND HEALTH BOARD None	—
TOTAL MIDLAND	—
MID-WESTERN HEALTH BOARD Day Hospital at Shelbourne Road, Limerick	14
TOTAL MID-WESTERN	14
NORTH-EASTERN HEALTH BOARD Day Centre, St. Davnet's Hospital, Monaghan Day Hospital, Cavan, Co. Cavan Day Centre, Dundalk, Co. Louth Day Centre, Drogheda, Co. Louth (held in St. Brigid's Hospital, Ardee pending the opening of a Centre in Drogheda)	24 35 26 17
TOTAL NORTH-EASTERN	102
NORTH-WESTERN HEALTH BOARD Day Centre/Day Hospital at St. Conal's Hospital, Letterkenny, Co. Donegal Day Centre/Day Hospital at St. Columba's Hospital, Sligo	15 20
TOTAL NORTH-WESTERN	35
SOUTH-EASTERN HEALTH BOARD Kelvin Grove Day Hospital, Carlow	40
TOTAL SOUTH-EASTERN	40
SOUTHERN HEALTH BOARD Ravenscourt Day Hospital, Cork St. Stephen's Hospital Day Hospital, Sarsfieldcourt, Cork Caherina House Day Hospital, Tralee, Co. Kerry	30 30 33
TOTAL SOUTHERN	93
WESTERN HEALTH BOARD Kilkerrin Support Centre, Co. Galway St. Michael's Day Hospital, St. Mary's Hospital, Castlebar, Co. Mayo Boyle Day Centre, Co. Roscommon St. Patrick's Day Hospital, Castlerea, Co. Roscommon St. Patrick's Day Centre, Castlerea, Co. Roscommon Day Hospital at Regional Hospital, Galway Carraroe Support Centre, Co. Galway Halla Naomh Padraic Support Centre, Galway	7 20 10 10 10 10 27 18
TOTAL WESTERN	112
GRAND TOTAL	1,180

(a) All of the Day Facilities in the EHB are operated by the Health Board unless otherwise stated.
Source: Department of Health.

Out-Patient Clinics

3.8   Table 12 compares national out-patient statistics in 1975, 1979 and 1983. A breakdown by health board area of the 1983 statistics is given in Table 13.

TABLE 12

Out-patient clinics: comparison of national psychiatric out-patient statistics 1975, 1979 and 1983

Year	Number of Clinic Locations	Number of Patients	Number of Attendances
1975	184	28,054	128,280
1979	205	37,597	183,437
1983	211	45,197	200,321

TABLE 13

Out-patient statistics for year ended 31st May 1983

Health Board	Number of Clinic Locations	Number of Patients	Number of Attendances
Eastern	43	20,991	118,835
Midland	20	2,037	9,189
Mid-Western	17	3,878	17,358
North-Eastern	9	2,161	7,890
North-Western	24	3,824	6,394
South-Eastern	33	3,480	17,936
Southern	28	4,000*	12,781
Western	37	4,826*	9,938*
Total	211	45,197	200,321

*Estimate.
Source: Department of Health.

Hostels

3.9   Table 14 compares the number of hostels for the mentally ill in 1981, 1982 and 1983. A breakdown by health board area of the 1983 statistics is given in Table 15.

TABLE 14

Hostels: Comparison of number of hostels for the mentally ill in 1981, 1982 and 1983

Health Board	1981	1982	1983
Eastern	28	30	32
Midland	3	6	7
Mid-Western	8	8	8
North-Eastern	20	19	20
North-Western	8	9	10
South-Eastern	15	15	16
Southern	8	6	6
Western	5	6	12
Total	95	99	111

TABLE 15
Hostels: Number of hostels for the mentally ill and number of places available 1983

Health Board	Number of Hostels	Number of Places	Number of Places per 100,000 population
Eastern	32	352	29.5
Midland	7	35	17.3
Mid-Western	8	99	32.1
North-Eastern	20	129	44.6
North-Western	10	66	31.7
South-Eastern	16	96	25.6
Southern	6	76	14.4
Western	12	89	26.1
Total	111	942	26.9

Note: The rates for the health boards are based on the 1981 population. The national rate is based on the estimate of the 1983 population.
Source: Department of Health.

Community Workshops/Sheltered Workshops

3.10   Table 16 compares the number of workshops available for mentally ill persons living in the community in 1981, 1982 and 1983.

TABLE 16

Community Workshops/Sheltered Workshops: Comparison of number of workshops available for mentally ill persons living in the community either at home or in a hostel setting 1981, 1982 and 1983.

Health Board	1981	1982	1983
Eastern	5	6	11
Midland	3	3	5
Mid-Western	3	3	4
North-Eastern	1	1	6
North-Western	8	8	9
South-Eastern	4	4	9
Southern	5	7	5
Western	2	3	4
Total	31	35	53

Note: The 1983 summary includes a number of Industrial Therapy Units attached to Psychiatric Hospitals and several Rehabilitation Institute Workshops which are not included in the 1981 and 1982 figures.
Source: Department of Health

(c) Staffing
Nursing Staff

3.11   Table 17 shows the number of staff in the four main nursing grades in each hospital and health board. Table 18 shows the number of senior nursing staff in each hospital and health board. Table 19 summarises the total number of nursing posts in the psychiatric service by grade.

TABLE 17
Nursing Staff employed in health board psychiatric hospitals on 1st April 1984.

Hospital and Health Board Area	Student Nurse M	F	Staff Nurse M	F	Deputy Charge Nurse	Deputy Ward Sister	Charge Nurse	Ward Sister	Total
St Brendan's	50	50	164	228	28	23	27	27	597
St Ita's	35	53	157	154	25	25	20	15	484
St Loman's	15	16	43	75	6	8	3	6	172
Newcastle	1	1	20	20	4	2	2	1	51
Eastern	101	120	384	477	63	58	52	49	1304
St Fintan's	1	4	71	61	10	9	9	9	174
St Loman's, Mullingar	7	14	135	124	16	11	14	13	334
Midland	8	18	206	185	26	20	23	22	508
St Joseph's	25	14	101	94	15	10	20	15	294
Our Lady's, Ennis	18	17	86	65	15	15	11	9	236
Mid-Western	43	31	187	159	30	25	31	24	530
St Davnet's	19	9	78	91	14	13	11	9	244
St Brigid's, Ardee	—	—	32	63	6	3	6	3	113
North-Eastern	19	9	110	154	20	16	17	12	357
St Columba's	14	19	86	84	18	10	15	11	257
St Conal's	11	17	71	81	20	18	16	16	250
North-Western	25	36	157	165	38	28	31	27	507
St Canice's	12	15	45	42	8	7	7	6	142
St Dympna's	5	4	34	51	9	7	8	8	126
St. Luke's	11	16	60	58	13	8	11	7	184
St. Otteran's	2	2	52	65	7	6	9	6	149
St Senan's	18	4	51	79	8	7	9	7	183
South-Eastern	48	41	242	295	45	35	44	34	784
Our Lady's Cork[a]	18	33	145	169	62	42	39	26	534
St Finan's	10	12	100	100	14	8	18	16	278
Southern	28	45	245	269	76	50	57	42	812
St. Brigid's, Ballinasloe	7	7	181	172	16	14	19	20	436
St Mary's[b]	4	13	83	98	15	11	16	10	250
St Patrick's	—	—	54	66	8	8	7	7	150
Western	11	20	318	336	39	33	42	37	836
TOTAL	283	320	1849	2040	337	265	297	247	5638
	603		3889		602		544		

[a]Figures include the psychiatric unit, Cork Regional Hospital.
[b]Figures include the psychiatric unit in Castlebar General Hospital.
Note: In addition to the above figures there are approximately 225 nurses working in psychiatric units attached to General Hospitals (excluding Cork Regional Hospital and Castlebar General Hospital).
Source: Department of Health.

TABLE 18

Senior nursing staff employed in health board psychiatric hospitals and units, November, 1984

Hospital/Unit and Health Board Area.	Assistant Chief Nursing Officer	Chief Nursing Officer	Total
St. Brendan's Hospital	13	2	15
St. Ita's Hospital	12	2	14
St. Loman's Hospital	6	2	8
Newcastle Hospital	4	1	5
Vergemount Unit ⎫ St. Dympna's Unit ⎭	Staffed by St. Brendan's Hospital		
St. Patrick's Hospital ⎫ (H.Bd.) ⎬ St. James's Unit ⎭	Staffed by St. Patrick's Hospital		
St. Vincent's Hospital, Fairview (H.Bd.)	Staffed by St. Vincent's Hospital		
St. John of God Hospital (H.Bd)	Staffed by St. John of God Hospital		
St. Vincent's Unit, Elm Park	1 Unit Nursing Officer	—	1
EASTERN	36	7	43
St. Fintan's Hospital, Portlaoise	7	1	8
St. Loman's Hospital, Mullingar	8	1	9
MIDLAND	15	2	17
St. Joseph's Hospital, Limerick	8	1	9
Our Lady's Hospital, Ennis	8	1	9
Unit at Limerick Regional Hospital	1 Asst. Matron	—	1
MID—WESTERN	17	2	19
St. Davnet's Hospital, Monaghan	8	1	9
St. Brigid's Hospital, Ardee	3	1	4
NORTH—EASTERN	11	2	13
St. Columba's Hospital, Sligo	6	1	7
St. Conal's Hospital, Letterkenny	7	1	8
Unit at Letterkenny General Hospital	Staffed by St. Conal's Hospital		
NORTH—WESTERN	13	2	15

Hospital/Unit and Health Board Area.	Assistant Chief Nursing Officer	Chief Nursing Officer	Total
St. Canice's Hospital, Kilkenny	7	1	8
St. Dympna's Hospital, Carlow	6	1	7
St. Luke's Hospital, Clonmel	7	1	8
St. Otteran's Hospital, Waterford	7	1	8
St. Senan's Hospital, Enniscorthy	7	1	8
St. Michael's Unit, Clonmel	1 Asst. Matron	—	1
St. Declan's Unit, Ardkeen	Staffed by St. Otteran's Hospital		
SOUTH—EASTERN	35	5	40
Our Lady's Hospital, Cork	12	3	15
St. Finan's Hospital, Killarney	6	1	7
St. Stephen's Unit, Sarsfieldcourt	1	1	2
St. Anne's Unit, Skibbereen Unit at Regional Hospital, Wilton	Staffed by Our Lady's Hospital		
SOUTHERN	19	5	24
St. Brigid's Hospital, Ballinasloe	12	1	13
St. Mary's Hospital, Castlebar	7	1	8
St. Patrick's Hospital, Castlerea	6	1	7
St. Theresa's Unit, Castlebar	Staffed by St. Mary's Hospital		
Unit at Regional Hospital, Galway.	1 Asst. Matron	—	1
WESTERN	26	3	29
GRAND TOTAL	172	28	200

Source: Department of Health

TABLE 19

Total Number of Nursing Posts Categorised by Grade

Grade	Number of Nurses
Student Nurses	603
Staff Nurses	3889
Ward Supervisory Posts (Including Deputies)	1146
Assistant Chief Nursing Officers	172
Nurses in above grades in general hospital units	225
Chief Nursing Officers	28
Community Psychiatric Nurses	169
TOTAL	6232

Source: Department of Health.

Consultant Psychiatrists

3.12 The number of approved consultant posts in general psychiatry in health board psychiatric hospitals and units in July 1984 is shown in Table 20.

TABLE 20

Number of Approved Consultant Posts in General Psychiatry in Health Board Psychiatric Hospitals and Units

Hospital and Health Board Area	Number of Approved Consultant Posts
St. Brendans (Team 1)	6
St. Brendan's & Vergemount (Team 2)	4
St. Brendan's & St. Vincents Fairview (Team 3)	4
St. Brendan's Special Interest	2
St. Dympna's Alcoholic Unit	2
Garden Hill (Research Unit)	3
St. Ita's, Portrane	5
St. Loman's, Palmerstown	7
Cluain Mhuire	5
Newcastle, Co. Wicklow	3
EASTERN (minus most of Co. Kildare)	41
St. Loman's, Mullingar	7
St. Fintan's, Portlaoise	4
Midland (plus Co. Meath)[a]	11
St. Joseph's, Limerick	5
Our Lady's, Ennis	4
MID-WESTERN (minus Tipperary North-Riding)	9
St. Davnet's, Monaghan	4
St. Brigid's, Ardee	4
NORTH-EASTERN (minus Co. Meath)	8
St. Conal's, Letterkenny	5
St. Columba's, Sligo	4
NORTH-WESTERN	9
St. Canice's, Kilkenny	3
St. Dympna's, Carlow	3
St. Luke's, Clonmel	4
St. Otteran's, Waterford	3
St. Senan's, Wexford	3
SOUTH-EASTERN (plus most of Kildare and Tipperary N.R.)[a]	16
St. Anne's Unit, Skibbereen	3
St. Stephen's, Sarsfieldcourt	4
Our Lady's Hospital, Cork	5
Psychiatric Unit, Cork Regional, Wilton	5
St. Finan's, Killarney	4
SOUTHERN	21

174

Hospital and Health Board Area	Number of Approved Consultant Posts
St. Brigid's, Ballinasloe	6
Psychiatric Unit, Galway Regional	3
St. Mary's, Castlebar	4
St. Patrick's, Castlerea	3
WESTERN	16
NATIONAL TOTAL	131

Note: Consultant psychiatrists employed in the psychiatric units in Limerick Regional Hospital, Letterkenny General Hospital, St. Joseph's Hospital, Clonmel, Waterford Regional Hospital and Castlebar General Hospital are included with the consultant complement of the psychiatric hospitals in those areas.

[a]The Midland and South-Eastern Health Boards provide psychiatric services for patients outside their areas. St. Loman's Hospital, Mullingar serves Co. Meath (North-Eastern Health Board). St. Dympna's Hospital, Carlow serves most of Co. Kildare (Eastern Health Board) and St. Luke's Hospital, Clonmel serves Tipperary North-Riding (Mid-Western Health Board).

Source: Department of Health.

Clinical Psychologists, Social Workers and Occupational Therapists

3.13   The number of clinical psychologists, social workers and occupational therapists employed in the psychiatric service in each health board is shown in Table 21.

TABLE 21

Number of Clinical Psychologists, Social Workers and Occupational Therapists Employed in the Psychiatric Service, September 1984 by Health Board Area.

Health Board Area	Clinical Psychologists	Social Workers	Occupational Therapists
Eastern	22	13	14
Midland	4[a]	—	1
Mid-Western	4	2	—
North-Eastern	3	—	3
North-Western	2	4	5
South-Eastern	5	—	3
Southern	6	5	12
Western	12	12	7.5[b]
TOTAL	58	36	45.5

[a]Includes one part-time clinical psychologist.
[b]One occupational therapist is assigned 50/50 to Special Hospital Care Programme and Community Care Programme.
Source: Department of Health.

Appendix 4

Estimating the Future Long-term Bed Needs for St. Ita's Hospital, Portrane

4.1 The following approach was adopted by a project team to estimate the bed needs for old long-stay patients at St. Ita's Hospital, Portrane.

4.2 The number of long-stay psychiatric patients, distributed by age, in St. Ita's Hospital at the end of 1982 is shown in Table 4.1.

TABLE 4.1

Existing Long-Stay Psychiatric Patients (excluding mentally handicapped) in St. Ita's Hospital, Portrane 31 December, 1982

Age	Total Number
Under 30 years	3
30-39	12
40-49	46
50-54	26
55-59	56
60-64	73
65-69	58
70-74	78
75-79	70
80-84	46
85 and over	21
TOTAL	489

4.3 The St. Ita's study team considered that, with adequate preparation, about 120 of these 489 patients should be capable of being discharged into a community setting. These would be largely from the under 60 age groups and would leave a total of about 370 long-stay psychiatric patients all aged over 55 years, who would need to remain as hospital in-patients. It could be expected that these would remain in the hospital until they died.

4.4 In order to estimate their life expectancy, age-specific mortality rates were calculated following an examination of the mortality experience of the hospital patients and compared with the mortality rates for the population of the State. The mortality rates used were:

176

Age	Annual Number of deaths per 1,000 corresponding population
All ages under 60	20
60-64	25
65-69	35
70-74	60
75-79	80
80-84	130
85 years and over	240

4.5   The application of these mortality rates would result in a reduction by death of the remaining long-stay patient population as follows:—

1983 — 369 patients

1988 — 265 patients

1993 — 177 patients

1998 — 107 patients

2003 — 57 patients

Appendix 5

Present Provision of Child Psychiatric Services

Eastern Health Board

5.1   There are three catchment areas for the delivery of child psychiatric services in the Eastern Health Board area, which are assigned to three different services:

1. Eastern Health Board Service, St. James Hospital
2. Mater Hospital Service.
3. Hospitaller Order of St. John of God Service, Orwell Road, Rathgar.

While each area has a comprehensive service, there is some flexibility in relation to the use of specialised units. The Mater Hospital Service and the St. John of God Service also provide a national child psychiatric service.

Eastern Health Board Child and Family Psychiatric Service

Catchment Area: Western County Dublin and South Kildare.

The Eastern Health Board has a Clinical Director in child psychiatry, four consultant child psychiatrists and a full complement of staff on its multidisciplinary teams servicing its out-patient clinics and residential centres. The main services are:

1. Department of Child Psychiatry, St. James's Hospital, Dublin which contains the clinical and administrative base of the service.

2. Ballyfermot Child and Family Centre.

3. Castleknock Child and Family Centre.

4. National Children's Hospital Child Guidance Clinic, Harcourt Street, Dublin.

5. Warrenstown House Residential Treatment Centre for Children and Young Adolescents, Dublin.

6. St. Loman's Hospital Child Psychiatric Unit and Ballyowen Meadows School, Palmerstown, Dublin.

178

Mater Hospital Child and Family Psychiatric Service

Catchment Area: North East City and County Dublin.

The main assessment and treatment services are:

1. The Department of Child and Family Psychiatry, Mater Hospital, Dublin. This is the clinical and administrative base and also contains a special school.

2. Child and Family Community Clinics, Ballymun.

3. St. Paul's Hospital and Special School, Beaumont.

4. St. Francis's Clinic, Children's Hospital, Temple Street, Dublin.

Assessment and consultative services are delivered to a wide range of medical, community and educational facilities including:

1. Our Lady's Treatment Unit (Community home for adolescent boys).

2. St. Vincent's Children's Home, Goldenbridge, Inchicore, Dublin 6. Group Homes at Phibsboro, Amiens Street and Talbot Houses.

3. Casa Catriona, a special national school at St. Mary's, Cabra, for deaf and language disordered children.

4. Many primary schools throughout the area.

Hospitaller Order of St. John of God

Catchment Area: South East City and County Dublin, Wicklow and North Kildare.

The staff include a Clinical Director, three full-time and two part-time consultant child psychiatrists, and full complement of multidisciplinary staff. Assessment and treatment resources include:

1. Child and Family Services, Orwell Road, Rathgar. This is the administrative and clinical headquarters, and includes a pre-school unit, a special primary school and a residential unit.

2. Child and Family Centre, Tallaght.

3. St. John of God Family Service Cluain Mhuire, Blackrock, Co. Dublin. As well as providing comprehensive psychiatric services to the South County Dublin area, this centre has a pre-school unit and in addition specialises in adolescent psychiatry with access to St. John of God's Hospital, Stillorgan for in-patients when required.

4. Our Lady's Hospital for Sick Children, Crumlin. Out-patient clinic and liaison and consultative child psychiatry to the hospital. Children are admitted to the hospital where required.

Midland Health Board

5.2   The service is provided by the board's consultant child psychiatrist, in association with psychologists and social workers from the community care programme on a part-time basis. The service headquarters is at St. Loman's Hospital, Mullingar, and regular clinics are held in Mullingar and in Tullamore, Athlone, Longford, Navan, Trim and when required in Portlaoise.

Mid-Western Health Board

5.3   The Mid-Western Health Board does not have its own child psychiatric service. Children with emotional problems are seen by the psychiatrists attached to the Brothers of Charity Services in Limerick, and others are referred to the child psychiatric services in Cork, Galway and at times to Dublin.

North-Eastern Health Board

5.4   The North-Eastern Health Board does not have its own child psychiatric service. However, County Meath is served by the child psychiatrist from the Midland Health Board. In addition, a child psychiatrist from Dublin holds a regular clinic in Dundalk.

North-Western Health Board

5.5   The North-Western Health Board does not have its own child psychiatric service. At present patients are referred to the Western Health Board Services, and also to child psychiatrists in Dublin.

South-Eastern Health Board

5.6   The South-Eastern Health Board does not have its own child psychiatric service. Outside child psychiatrists hold clinics within the Health Board area liaising with the board's own community care psychologists and social workers. In this way child psychiatrists from Dublin service clinics in Wexford and Kilkenny, and a child psychiatrist from Cork holds a clinic in Clonmel.

Southern Health Board

5.7   There are two catchment areas for the delivery of child psychiatric services in the Southern Health Board area which are assigned to two different services:

1. Southern Health Board Child Psychiatric Service.
2. Brothers of Charity Service.

Southern Health Board Child Psychiatric Service

Catchment Area: North Lee area of Cork City and North County Cork.

Pending the recruitment of a consultant child psychiatrist, consultants from the Brothers of Charity provide consultant cover to the nuclear child guidance team. Services include:

1. The Young People's Residential Unit at St. Stephen's Hospital, Sarsfieldcourt, for assessment and treatment of emotionally disturbed children and adolescents.

2. Regular child guidance clinics are held in Cork city twice weekly, and on a monthly basis in Mallow and Bantry.

Brothers of Charity Service

Catchment Area: South Lee area of Cork City, West Cork and County Kerry.

The Brothers of Charity have two consultant child psychiatrists with a full complement of staff on the multidisciplinary teams. Services include:

1. Our Lady of Good Counsel, Lota, Glanmire, Co. Cork. This is the clinical and administrative base for this service. There is an assessment and treatment unit with special schools for children with autism, developmental delays, communication disorder and mental handicap. Regular clinics are held.

2. Child and Family Clinic, Victoria Road, Cork. This provides a regular child psychiatric service with a pre-school unit for children with communication disorder, developmental delay and behaviour disorders.

3. Marymount Training Centre, Cork, Residential Unit for Junior Adolescent Girls. In addition, consultative services are offered to a wide range of community and educational facilities, including community hostels for adolescents.

Western Health Board

5.8 The service is delivered by the Western Health Board's child and adolescent pyschiatric staff. These include a Clinical Director, a consultant child psychiatrist with two multidisciplinary teams and other staff.

Assessment and treatment resources include:

1. St. Annes' Children's Centre, Taylor's Hill, Galway. The clinical and administrative headquarters is located here. In addition there is a special primary school. It has a day and residential assessment and

treatment unit for pre-adolescent and adolescent children, and in addition out-patient clinics are held.

2. Lyradoon Family Centre, 65 Lower Salthill, Galway.

3. Department of Child and Family Psychiatry, Regional Hospital, Galway. This provides consultative and liaison child psychiatry in the hospital with access to beds when required. In addition, out-patient clinics are held.

4. Regular out-patient clinics are held in: Health Centre, Ballinasloe; County Clinic, Roscommon; County Clinic, Castlebar; Health Centre, Ballina; Ionad Shlainte, An Ceathru Rua.

Assessment and consultative services are delivered to a wide range of medical, community and educational facilities including:

—St. Joseph's Residential Home, Lower Salthill, Galway.

—Aisling Residential Home, Ballyloughane Road, Renmore, Galway.

References

Chapter 1

1. Department of Health, Dublin. Annual Statistics.
2. Tooth, G. C. and Brooke, E. Trends in the mental hospital population and their effects on future planning. Lancet 1, 1961 710-713.
3. Department of Health. Commission of Inquiry on Mental Illness. 1966. Dublin, Stationery Office.
4. Norman, C. The Domestic Treatment of the Insane. 1896. Dublin.
5. Department of Health. Report of the Inspector of Mental Hospitals for the year 1950. Dublin, Stationery Office.
6. Department of Health. Report of the Commission of Inquiry on Mental Handicap. 1965. Dublin, Stationery Office.
7. Department of Health. The Care of the Aged. Report of an Interdepartmental Committee. 1968. Dublin, Stationery Office.
8. Third Interim Report of the Interdepartmental Committee on Mentally Ill and Maladjusted Persons. 1978. Dublin, Stationery Office.
9. Department of Health, Services for the Mentally Handicapped. Report of a Working Party. 1980. Dublin, Stationery Office.
10. National Health Services. A Hospital Plan for England and Wales. 1962. London, Her Majesty's Stationery Office.
11. Department of Health and Social Security. Providing a Comprehensive District Psychiatric Service for the Adult Mentally Ill. 1974. London, Her Majesty's Stationery Office.
12. Department of Health and Social Security. Better Services for the Mentally Ill. 1975. London, Her Majesty's Stationery Office.
13. Ramon, S. Psichiatria democratica: a case study of an Italian community mental health service. International Journal of Health Services, 1983, Volume 13, Number 2.
14. Jones, K. and Poletti, A. The mirage of a reform. New Society, 1984, 4 October.
15. Department of Health. Outline of the Future Hospital System. Report of the Consultative Council on the General Hospital Services, 1968. Dublin, Stationery Office.
16. Department of Health, Dublin. Report of the Working Party on Occupational Therapy/Industrial Therapy Services within the Psychiatric Service. November 1981.

Chapter 3

1. World Health Organisation. Changing Patterns in Mental Health Care, 1980. Copenhagen, Regional Office for Europe.
2. Department of Health and Social Security. Providing a Comprehensive District Psychiatric Service for the Adult Mentally Ill. 1974. London, Her Majesty's Stationery Office.

3. Creer, C. Sturt, E. and Wykes, T. The role of relatives. Long-term community care: experience in a London borough. Psychological Medicine, 1982, Monograph Supplement 2, Cambridge University Press.

4. Byrne, L. O'Connor, T. and Fahy, T. J. The home behaviour of schizophrenic patients living in the community and attending a day centre. The British Journal of Psychiatry 1974, 125, 20-24.

5. Sainsbury, P. and Grad, J. Evaluating the Community Psychiatric Service in Chichester. Evaluating the Effectiveness of Mental Health Services (ed. Gruenberg E) Milbank Memorial Fund Quarterly, 1966 44, Part 2, No. 1.

Chapter 4

1. Community Psychiatric Nursing Service. Report of Review Group. 1984. Local Government Staff Negotiations Board.

Chapter 5

1. Fry, J. Profiles of Disease. Edinburgh and London: Livingstone, 1966.

2. Shepherd, M. Cooper, A.B. Brown, A.C. and Kalton, G. Psychiatric Illness in General Practice. 1966. London, Oxford University Press.

3. Department of Health and Social Security. Better Services for the Mentally Ill. 1975. London, Her Majesty's Stationery Office.

4. Locke, B.Z. Patients, psychiatric problems and non-psychiatrist physicians in a pre-paid group practice program. American Journal of Psychiatry, August 1955; 123:2 207-210.

5. Locke, B.Z. and Gardner, E.P. Psychiatric disorders among the patients of general practitioners and internists. Public Health Report, February, 1969; 84.2 167-173.

6. Goldberg, D. and Huxley, P. Mental Illness in the Community. 1980. Tavistock Publications.

7. Comber, H. Boland, M. Shannon, W. Psychotropic drug prescribing in Irish general practice: a study in peer-group continuing education. Irish Medical Journal, May 1984, 77, 5, 147-150.

8. Goldberg, D. Blackwell, B. Psychiatric illness in general practice. British Medical Journal 1970, 439-43.

9. Fahy, T. J. Pathways of specialist referral of depressed patients from General Practice. The British Journal of Psychiatry 1974, 124, 231-239.

10. Walsh, D. O'Hare, A. Blake, B. Halpenny, J.V. and O'Brien, P.F. The treated prevalence of mental illness in the Republic of Ireland — the Three County Case Register study. Psychological Medicine 1980, 10, 465-470.

11. World Health Organisation. Psychiatry and Primary Medical Care. Report of Working Group, Copenhagen 1973.

12. Department of Health. Report of the Working Party on the General Medical Service, 1984. Dublin Stationery Office.

13. Reid, P. The management of patients' psychological problems by their general practitioners. Irish Medical Journal, June, 1983, Volume 76, Number 6.

14. World Health Organisation. Changing Patterns in Mental Health Care. Report of a Working Group, Copenhagen 1980.
15. Cooper, J.E. Crisis Admission Units and Emergency Psychiatric Services. World Health Organisation, Copenhagen 1979.

Chapter 6

1. Hassall, C. Psychiatric day hospital care. In: The Care of the Mentally Disordered: an Examination of Some Alternatives to Hospital Care 1979 edited by M.R. Olsen. Birmingham, B.A.S.W. Publications, 111-129.
2. Department of Health. Commission of Inquiry on Mental Illness. 1966. Dublin, Stationery Office.
3. National Day Care Project. Adult day care: selected reading. 1978. National Institute for Social Work, 5/7 Tavistock Place, London WC1.
4. Department of Health and Social Security. Day Care for the Mentally Ill, March 1980. Discussion paper.
5. Gath, D.H. Hassall, C. and Cross, K.W. Whither psychiatric day care: A study of day patients in Birmingham. British Medical Journal 1973, i, 94-98.
6. World Health Organisation. Changing Patterns in Mental Health Care, 1980. Copenhagen, Regional Office for Europe.
7. Department of Health and Social Security. Better Services for the Mentally Ill. 1975. London, Her Majesty's Stationery Office.
8. Wing, J.K. (editor): Long-term community care: experience in a London borough. Psychological Medicine. Monograph Supplement 2, 1982. Cambridge University Press.
9. Vaughan, P.J. The disordered development of day care in psychiatry. Health Trends 1983, 15, 91-94.
10. Wilkinson, G. Day care for patients with psychiatric disorders. British Medical Journal 1984, Volume 288, 9 June.

Chapter 7

1. Department of Health, Dublin. Annual Statistics.
2. The 1963 Irish Psychiatric Hospital Census. The Medico-Social Research Board, Dublin.
3. The Irish Psychiatric Hospital Census 1971. The Medico-Social Research Board, Dublin.
4. Irish Psychiatric Hospitals and Units Census 1981. The Medico-Social Research Board, Dublin.
5. Activities of Irish Psychiatric Hospitals and Units, 1970. The Medico-Social Research Board, Dublin.
6. Activities of Irish Psychiatric Hospitals and Units, 1982. The Medico-Social Research Board, Dublin. (Unpublished).
7. Zubin, P. Magaziner, J. and Steinhauer, S. R. The metamorphosis of schizophrenia: from chronicity to vulnerability. Psychological Medicine 1983, 13,551-13,571.

8. Gagné, O. and Diathine, R. World Health Organisation. Paper prepared for 8th meeting on Mental Health Services in Pilot Study Areas, Mannheim 1981.

9. Department of Health and Social Security. Better Services for the Mentally Ill, 1975. London, Her Majesty's Stationery Office.

10. The provision of in-patient facilities for the mentally ill — a paper to assist National Health Service planners — Department of Health and Social Security 1981. Unpublished.

11. Mental Illness: Policies for Prevention, Treatment, Rehabilitation and Care. Department of Health and Social Security (MHA) March 1983.

12. Guidelines for Psychiatric Treatment in the Eighties: Opinions of the Social Welfare Board, 1980: 2. Socialstyrelsen Stockholm 1980.

13. Walsh, D. Butler, S. and Starks, S. The St. Loman's psychiatric service: an exercise in parsimony. Irish Journal of Psychiatry, Autumn 1981.

14. Owens, J. M. Problems in restructuring of psychiatric services. Irish Journal of Psychiatry, Autumn 1984.

15. Services for the Mentally Handicapped. Report of a Working Party. 1980. Dublin, Stationery Office.

16. McGennis, A. J., Browne, I. W., O'Callaghan, J., Hartman, M. L. and Tedders, J. G. Screening psychiatric admissions: 6-months experience in the assessment centre of a large urban psychiatric hospital, Journal of the Irish Medical Association, September 1980, Volume 73, No. 9.

17. McGennis, A. Browne, I. Hartman, M. O'Shea, B. and O'Rourke, M. Emergency psychiatric admissions: the value of a special assessment unit. Unpublished.

18. McGennis, A. Effect of the first three years of the assessment centre in reducing admissions to St. Brendan's Hospital. Irish Journal of Psychiatry 1983, 3, 1, 18-23.

Chapter 8

1. Department of Health, Dublin. Annual Statistics.

2. Walsh, D. Butler, S. and Starks, S. The St. Loman's psychiatric service: an exercise in parsimony. Irish Journal of Psychiatry. Autumn 1981.

3. Walsh, D., O'Hare, A., Blake, B., Halpenny, J. V. and O'Brien, P. F. The treated prevalence of mental illness in the Republic of Ireland — the Three County Case Register study. Psycnological Medicine 1980, 10,465-470.

4. Keane, P. and Fahy, T. J. Who receives the aftercare? Utilisation of services by discharged in-patients. Psychological Medicine 1982, 12, 891-902.

Chapter 9

1. Owens, J. M. Problems in restructuring of psychiatric services. Irish Journal of Psychiatry, Autumn 1984.

2. Pritlove, J. Accommodation without resident staff for ex-psychiatric patients: changing trends and needs. British Journal of Social Work 1983, Volume 13, No. 1.

3. Hynes, M. Report on a Council of Europe Fellowship visit to Finland. 1980. Unpublished.

4. Hunt, A. Boarding out—the way to an independent lifestyle. Health and Social Services Journal, June 14, 1984.

5. Olsen, R. Boarding out the long-stay psychiatric patient. In Differential Approaches in Social Work with the Mentally Disordered. (Ed. R. Olsen) 1976. BASW, Birmingham.

6. Ryan, P. and Hewett, S.H. A pilot study of hostels for the mentally ill. Social Work Today 1976, 6, 774-778.

7. Department of Health and Social Security. Better Services for the Mentally Ill. 1975. London, Her Majesty's Stationery Office.

Chapter 10

1. Department of Health. Report of the Working Party on Occupational Therapy/Industrial Therapy Services within the Psychiatric Service. November 1981.

2. Department of Health, Dublin. Annual Statistics.

3. Department of Health. Training and Employing the Handicapped. Report of a Working Party established by the Minister for Health. 1975. Dublin, Stationery Office.

4. Towards a Full Life. Green Paper on Services for Disabled People. 1984. Dublin, Stationery Office.

Chapter 11

1. Population and Labour Force Projections 1986 and 1991. Inter-Departmental Group on Population Projection (forthcoming).

2. Organisation of Comprehensive Community-based Mental Health Services for the Elderly with Mental Disabilities. Dr. C. Godber. WHO Working Group on Mental Health Care of the Elderly, Cork 3-7 October, 1983.

3. Kay, D.W.K. et al. Old age mental disorders in Newcastle-upon-Tyne, British Journal of Psychiatry 1964, 110, 146-158.

4. Cooper, B. and Schwarz, R.: Psychiatric case identification in an elderly urban population, Social Psychiatry 1982, 17, 43-52.

5. Svanborg, A. et al. Epidemiological Studies on Social and Medical Conditions: Report on a Survey. Copenhagen, WHO Regional Office for Europe 1982. Euro Reports and Studies No. 62.

6. Kay, D.W.K. et al. Mental illness and hospital usage in the elderly: a random sample followed up. Comprehensive Psychiatry 1970, I, 26-35.

7. Gurland, B., Copeland, J. and Kuriensky, J.: The Mind and Mood of Aging. Groom Helm, London, 1983.

8. Irish Psychiatric Hospital and Units Census, 1981, Medico-Social Research Board, Dublin.

9. Binchy, I. and Walsh, D. A prevalence study of psycho-geriatric illness in an area of Dublin. Journal of the Irish Medical Association, 1977, 70, 9, 287-295.

10. Activities of Irish Psychiatric Hospitals and Units, 1982. The Medico Social Research Board, Dublin. (Unpublished).

11. The Care of the Aged—Report of an Inter-Departmental Committee. 1968. Dublin, Stationery Office.

12. Guidelines for collaboration between geriatric physicians and psychiatrists in the care of the elderly. The Bulletin of the Royal College of Psychiatrists, October, 1979.

13. Services to prevent Disability in the Elderly—WHO Meeting in Sokobanja, October, 1982.

14. Day Hospital Care, Report Number 1, National Council for the Aged, April, 1982.

15. Retirement: A General Review, Report Number 2, National Council for the Aged, December, 1982.

16. Community Services for the Elderly, Report Number 3, National Council for the Aged, September, 1983.

17. Retirement Age: Fixed or Flexible? Report Number 4, National Council for the Aged, Seminar, February, 1983.

18. The World of the Elderly: the Rural Experience, Report Number 5, National Council for the Aged, May 1984.

19. Incomes of the Elderly in Ireland, Report Number 6, National Council for the Aged, May 1984.

20. The provision of In-Patient Facilities for the Mentally Ill — a paper to assist NHS planners — Department of Health and Social Security (Unpublished).

Chapter 12

1. Department of Health. Commission of Inquiry on Mental Illness. 1966. Dublin, Stationery Office.

2. Rutter, M. Tizard, J. and Whitmore, K. (eds) 1970. Epidemiology of psychiatric disorder: Education, Health and Behaviour. London: Longmans.

3. McCarthy, P. Fitzgerald, M. and Smith, M.A., Prevalence of childhood autism in Ireland. Irish Medical Journal, May 1984, Volume 77, No. 5.

4. Ministry of Education. Underwood Report. 1955. London, Her Majesty's Stationery Office.

5. Brandon, S. An epidemiological study of maladjustment in childhood. 1960. Unpublished M.D. Thesis, University of Durham.

6. Garside, Hulbert, Kilvin, van der Spuy, Wolstenholme and Wrate. An evaluation of psychiatric services for children, England and Wales, in Wing and Hailey, Evaluation of Psychiatric Services. O.U.P. 1973.

7. Rutter, M. et al. Attainment and adjustment in two geographical areas: I, II and III. British Journal of Psychiatry 1975, 126, 493-533.

8. News and Notes. Royal College of Psychiatrists. Norms for staffing of psychiatric services: 3. Child Psychiatry. British Journal of Psychiatry, 1973, 4-3.

9. The College. Providing a district service for child and adolescent psychiatry: medical manpower priority — Bulletin of the Royal College of Psychiatrists. May 1983.

10. Development of Community Mental Health Services — Planned Evolution. Eastern Health Board, March 1978.

11. Interim Reports of the Interdepartmental Committee on mentally Ill and Maladjusted Persons 1974-1978. Stationery Office, Dublin.

12. First Interim Report of the Interdepartmental Committee on Mentally Ill and Maladjusted Persons. 1974. Stationery Office, Dublin.

13. Kanner, L. Autistic Disturbance of Affective Contact. Nervous Child 1943: 2:217-250.
14. Kolvin, I. and Kolvin et al. Studies in the Childhood Psychoses. British Journal of Psychiatry 1971, 118, 381-419.
15. Rutter, M. Concepts of Autism. A Review of Research. Journal of Child Psychology and Psychiatry, 1968, 9, 1-25.
16. Reifler, C.B. Epidemiological aspects of college mental health. J.AM. Coll. Health Assoc. 19:1590, 1971.
17. Farnsworth, D.L., Psychiatry, Education and the Young Adult. Charles C. Thomas, Springfield, Ill. 1966.

Chapter 13

1. The Medico-Social Research Board, Dublin. Unpublished.
2. The Irish Psychiatric Hospitals and Units Census 1981. The Medico-Social Research Board, Dublin.
3. Walsh, D. Alcohol-Related Medico-Social Problems and their Prevention. Copenhagen. WHO, Regional Office for Europe, 1982.
4. Activities of Irish Psychiatric Hospitals and Units 1965 — 1969. The Medico-Social Research Board, Dublin.
5. An Roinn Slainte. Annual Reports on Vital Statistics. Dublin, Stationery Office.
6. Garda Commissioner's Report on Crime 1950-1982.
7. Walsh, B. M. Drinking in Ireland. The Economic and Social Research Institute. September 1980.
8. Activities of Irish Psychiatric Hospitals and Units, 1978. The Medico-Social Research Board, Dublin.
9. Activities of Irish Psychiatric Hospitals and Units, 1980. The Medico-Social Research Board, Dublin.
10. Activities of Irish Psychiatric Hospitals and Units, 1982. The Medico-Social Research Board, Dublin. (Unpublished).
11. World Health Organisation. Problems Related to Alcohol Consumption, Report of a WHO Expert Committee. Technical Report Series 650. Geneva: WHO, 1980.
12. Baekeland, F., Lundwall, L. and Kissin, B. Methods for the treatment of chronic alcoholism: a critical appraisal. Research Advances in Alcohol and Drug Problems Vol. 2. (Eds.) R.J. Gibbens, Israel, H. Kalant et al. New York: John Wiley & Sons, 1975.
13. Orford, J. and Edwards, G. Alcoholism. Oxford University Press, 1977.
14. Report of the Working Party on the General Medical Service. 1984. Dublin, Stationery Office.
15. Davies, P. and Walsh, D. Alcohol Problems and Alcohol Control in Europe. Croom Helm, London, 1982.
16. Magee, D. and Leahy, A. Medical Services for Homeless People, 1975.
17. Homeless and Vulnerable-Medical Services for the Homeless. Simon Community, 1984.
18. Walsh, D. Amphetamine dependence in Dublin. Journal of the Irish Medical Association. 1966, 58, 347, 161-164.

19. Report of Working Party on Drug Abuse, 1971, Dublin, Stationery Office.
20. Report of the Committee on Drug Education, April 1974, Dublin, Stationery Office.
21. Government Statement on the Report of the Special Government Task Force on Drug Abuse, 20 September 1983. Government Information Service.
22. Nomenclature and classification of drug and alcohol-related problems: a W.H.O. Memorandum. Bulletin of the World Health Organisation 1981 59 (2), 225-242.
23. Byers, G. Report to: Task Force on Drug Abuse, 1982. Unpublished.
24. Shelley, E.B., O'Rourke, A. and Wilson-Davis, K. Drugs — a study in Dublin post-primary schools. Irish Medical Journal, 1982, 75, 254-9.
25. Shelley, E.B., Wilson-Davis, K., O'Rourke, A. and O'Rourke, F. Drugs — a study in post-primary schools situated outside Dublin, 1981. Irish Medical Journal, 1984, 77, 16.19.
26. Bradshaw, J. Dean, G. and Lavelle, P. Drug Misuse in Ireland, 1982-1983. Investigation in a North Central Dublin area and in Galway, Sligo and Cork, 1983. The Medico-Social Research Board, Dublin.
27. Dean, G. and Smith, R. Heroin Use in a Dun Laoghaire Borough Area 1983-84. 1984. The Medico-Social Research Board, Dublin.
28. Department of Health, Dublin.
29. Garda Commissioner's Report on Crime — various years.
30. Diagnostic and Statistical Manual of Mental Disorders. Third Edition. American Psychiatric Association, 1984.
31. Annual Reports of the General Medical Services (Payments) Board, Dublin.

Chapter 14

1. Department of Health Dublin — Psychiatric Services Staffing Questionnaire, April 1984.
2. Procedural Agreement on Integration, September 1984. Local Government Staff Negotiations Board.

Chapter 16

1. Latey, R.H. and Fahy, T.J. Electroconvulsive Therapy in the Republic of Ireland, 1982. (In press 1984).
2. World Health Organisation. Changing Patterns in Mental Health Care, 1980. Copenhagen, Regional Office for Europe.
3. Rutter, M. Shaffer, D. and Sturge, C. A Guide to a Multi-axial Classification in Childhood and Adolescence. Institute of Psychiatry, London.

Appendix 1

1. In-Patient Statistics. Mental Health Enquiry for England 1977. Department of Health and Social Security. 1980. Statistical and Research Report Series No. 3.
2. Statistiques Medicales des Services Psychiatriques. INSERM 1982.
3. Dupont, A. Institute of Psychiatric Demography, Aarhus, Denmark.
4. Irish Psychiatric Hospitals and Units Census, 1981. The Medico-Social Research Board, Dublin.
5. Activities of Irish Psychiatric Hospitals and Units, 1981. The Medico-Social Research Board, Dublin.
6. Activities of Irish Psychiatric Hospitals and Units, 1982. The Medico-Social Research Board, Dublin. (Unpublished).
7. Fuller-Torrey, E. McGuire, M. O'Hare, A. Walsh, D. and Spellman, M.P. Endemic psychosis in western Ireland. American Journal of Psychiatry 1984, Volume 141, Number 8, 966-970.
8. Ni Nullain, M. Buckley, H. McHugh, B. O'Hare, A. and Walsh D. Methodology for a study of mental illness in Ireland. Irish Journal of Psychiatry, Spring 1984, 4-9.
9. Epidemiology of Mental Disorders in Camberwell. Bebbington, Paul et al. Psychological Medicine 1981, 11, 561-579.
10. Robins, L.N. Helzer, J.E. Weissman, M.M. Orvaschel, H. Gruenberg, E. Burke Jr. J.D. and Regier, D.A. Lifetime Prevalence of Specific Psychiatric Disorders in Three Sites. Archives of General Psychiatry, October 1984, Vol. 41, No. 10, pp. 949-958.

Appendix 2

1. Department of Education. The Education of Children who are Handicapped by Impaired Hearing. 1972. Dublin, Stationery Office.
2. Denmark, J.C. Early profound deafness and mental retardation. The British Journal of Mental Subnormality 1978, Volume XXIV, Part II, Number 47.
3. Robinson, L.D. Sound Minds in a Soundless World. United States Department of Health, Education and Welfare, Public Health Service, Alcohol, Drug Abuse and Mental Health Administration 1978, National Institute of Mental Health.
4. Copper, A.F. Deafness in psychiatric illness. British Journal of Psychiatry 1976, 129, 216-226.
5. Grinker, P.R. Psychiatric Diagnosis Therapy and Research on the Psychotic Deaf. United States Department of Health, Education and Welfare, Social and Rehabilitation Services, Administration 1969, Washington D.C. 20201.
6. Denmark, J.C. Mental illness and early profound deafness. British Journal of Medical Psychology, 1966, 39, 117-124.
7. Denmark, J.C. and Warren, F. Psychiatric unit for the deaf. British Journal of Psychiatry 1972, 120, 423-428.
8. Rainer, J.D. Diagnostic considerations in psychiatric work for the deaf — psychiatric examination. Psychiatry and the Deaf, 1967. United States Department of Health, Education and Welfare, Social and Rehabilitation Service.
9. McCaul, E. Deaf patients in psychiatric hospitals. Thesis for Diploma in Community Education, 1983. St. Patrick's College, Maynooth. Unpublished.

GR. 30-02 S.O. 162738 1,000 Brunswick Press Ltd. 7/89